LOVE, MARRIAGE AND THE FAMILY

LOVE, MARRIAGE
AND
THE FAMILY

*

KENNETH WALKER

ODHAMS PRESS LIMITED

LONG ACRE, LONDON

CONTENTS

ILLUSTRATIONS

PREFACE

THE Victorian silence on the subject of sexuality was broken at the beginning of this century by a clatter of Freudian talk on the forbidden subject. Such a reaction was to be expected and if at times these Freudian chatterers forgot that modesty was not invented by Victorian prudes but was an entirely natural and necessary correlate to sexuality, their outspokenness was preferable to the hypocrisy and ultra-respectability of the preceding era.

As a result of this freedom of talk and of the many books written in the earlier decades of this century we have got rid, to a certain extent, of the notion that sexuality is a thoroughly disreputable and immoral affair. But only to a certain extent, for doctors and psychiatrists, whose business it is to deal with such problems, are still having to treat patients for sex-neuroses acquired as a result of having been reared in homes in which the Victorian attitude to sex still lingered. Indeed it is no exaggeration to say that the roots from which the neuroses of these patients have grown can often be traced back into nurseries and schoolrooms of homes of this kind. This is one of the reasons which has compelled me to go far beyond the frontiers originally marked out for this book. There exists a continuity in our emotional and sexual lives which makes it necessary to treat them as wholes. One finds that the difficulties which arise in the child-parent relationship are liable to crop up again later in the husband-wife relationship, and still later in the relationship of the parents to the next generation. So a book which was originally planned to deal only with love and marriage grew into a work which is concerned also with the family resulting from that love and marriage and includes also chapters on heredity, divorce and the sex education of children.

At one time I considered also the advisability of including in the book a chapter on the important subject of sex-ethics, but eventually decided against this. My reason for not doing this was that books on the subject of sex too often become vehicles for the propagation of the author's particular variety of morality. I have therefore contented myself with giving the facts, so far as I could see them, and have left it to the reader to draw his own conclusions, ethical and otherwise, from these facts. It will be for him or her to decide how the many problems which sexuality provides can best be dealt with. It is true that I sometimes make suggestions but they are suggestions with which the reader is fully entitled to disagree.

In only one instance have I been guilty of propaganda, namely in my pleading for greater tolerance in judging the sexual behaviour of other people. I have shown that there has never been and is never likely to be a standard pattern of sexual behaviour and yet in our judgement of the private lives of our fellow men and women we frequently display all the narrowness and the lack of charity of the Scribes and Pharisees. It was in order to drive home this lesson of our uncharitableness that I have included a short chapter on the problems of inter-sex.

Within the text I have acknowledged my indebtedness to the various authorities whom I have quoted, but here I should like to make special mention of the following works, which have been of special assistance to me in the writing of this book; Walter de la Mare's well-known symposium entitled *Love*, (Faber & Faber), *Any Wife and Any Husband* by Medica (Heinemann), *Woman: Man's Equal* by Sir Adolphe Abrahams (Christopher Johnson), *Ideal Marriage* by Dr. Van de Velde (Heinemann), and *Love without Fear* by Eustace Chesser (Rich & Cowan).

1

LOVE

THIS book is about love, marriage and the family, and it is important that we should agree, as far as it is possible for us to do so, what these three words mean. Now, although we have no difficulty at all defining the words marriage and the family, there has always been, and still is, a great deal of confusion and difference of opinion about the meaning of the word love. The truth is that love is one of those portmanteau words into which a number of emotions have been crammed. There is no word which has been used more loosely, been more abused and has given rise to more misunderstanding. It has been employed for a great many things; for the saint's search for the Divine Reality behind the screen of appearances, for the patriot's devotion to his own fatherland, for the fondness shown by a mother for her child, for the protective feeling that an elder brother may develop for his younger sister, for the sexual longing of a lover for his mistress and for the quiet devotion of an elderly couple to each other after many years of marriage, and for a great many other things besides. All of these diverse feelings have been grouped together under the single heading of love.

In this book we are concerned almost entirely with the love of a man for a woman and of a woman for a man, but even when we have narrowed down the meaning of the word to this, it will not always be easy to know precisely what we are talking about, for a great many different elements may enter into love between the two sexes.

We are still very ignorant about the nature of the strange force which draws a man to a woman and a woman to a man. If we were to question a number of different experts on this subject, the answers we should receive would vary with the person to whom we had addressed our enquiry. For example, if we asked a biologist about the nature of sexual love, he would answer that it was Nature's artful method of bringing the male and female together and thus securing a continuation of the species. Love, he would say, is synonymous with sexual attraction. He might then go on to point out to us that the lowest forms of life reproduced themselves in the simplest possible way, merely by splitting down the middle so that each half became a new individual. With this elementary method of reproduction there was no need for the existence of an attractive force between the two sexes, for the simple reason that there were no such things as sexes.

On a higher level of the evolutionary scale, a new and more elaborate form of reproduction began, namely sexual reproduction. The biologist would then point out that there were great advantages attached to this new form of reproduction and that the process we call evolution would have been unable to proceed without it. "Evolution", he would say, "depends for its success on a plentiful supply of variations to work upon and this can only be provided by a sexual form of reproduction. Let us suppose that two simple unicellular organisms managed to reproduce in themselves ten variations as material upon which the evolutionary machinery can get to work. These ten variations would give Nature very little scope for her work of bringing new patterns of life into being, but if instead of merely splitting down the middle, the two organisms in question were under the obligation of meeting and fusing together before it was possible for them to split into new individuals, then by the combined pooling of their variations Nature would be provided with much richer material on which to start work. The biologist might then end by saying that it was because the advantages conferred by sexual methods of reproduction were so great, that they were introduced at a very early stage of the evolutionary story. This in turn necessitated the creation of some mutual attraction between the two sexes in order to ensure their coming together and carrying out Nature's work. It will be noted that the biologist has made the attraction between the sexes entirely subservient to reproduction and evolution.

If we had afterwards sought out a psychologist to question about the nature of the attraction which drew a man towards a woman and a woman towards a man, he would answer quite differently. He would probably begin by saying that what brought the two together was a blind urge in the subconscious regions of their minds, an urge to which Freud had given the name libido. It was an urge as insistent and automatic as hunger and appeared in the individual at a very early age. He might then go on to say that the more conscious parts of the minds of the two people concerned did not necessarily approve of what was happening to them, but that the restraining force which these more conscious regions of the mind were able to exert was often so weak that it was quite unable to counteract what was happening. In other words, the psychologist would explain sexual love in terms of psychological drives, conflicts and compulsions.

Should we question him still further on the subject of this attraction between the sexes, and enquire of him what physical events were taking place in the body in association with it, he might describe to us the ductless glands and the action of their secretions on the body. When asked to be more explicit on this rather difficult subject, he would probably add that of all the ductless glands the reproductive glands, namely the testicles and the ovaries, were of the greatest importance in this connexion, since their secretions exerted a stimulating action on the sexual organs and thereby gave rise to sexual desires. This would be the sort of account a psychologist and an endocrinologist would give us of the phenomenon known as love between the sexes.

But after we had examined critically the answers received from these and other experts, we should find that they had really added very little to our knowledge of sexual love and had confused as much as enlightened us. All that they had said was that from the evolutionary standpoint, sexual reproduction was greatly preferable to asexual forms of reproduction, and that sexual excitement was associated with the occurrence of certain physiological changes in the body. These were facts of which we were previously aware so that little that is new has been learnt.

We should have been able to recognize the feelings and changes which these experts had described if they had happened in our own persons, but we should never have grasped what love was like from their descriptions alone. If we have had a personal experience of love, the experts' accounts of it seem to be as little related to what happened to us as the anatomist's account of the brain seem to be related to our minds.

None of the experts explains to us what we want to know most; why ninety-nine women leave a man as cold and indifferent to them as if they were statues, whilst a single glance from a hundredth woman renders him her slave for life. No, neither the scientist nor the psychologist is of any use to us in explaining the vagaries of love. Even the definition of love given by a French psychologist is woefully thin and unsatisfying, and the French seem to know more about the mystery of love between the sexes than does any other nation. All that Ribot is able to say in his well-known book on psychology is that love "is a sthenic emotion with physical characteristics which connect it on the one hand with joy, and on the other with tenderness".

The chemists tell us that the elements also have their affinities and that they seek satisfaction in combining in different ways. For example, an unwed atom of chlorine goes out into the world eager to find an unattached atom of sodium, and when these two solitary elements happen to meet nothing can keep them apart. Why not look therefore upon the riddle of human love in a similar manner and seek no explanation other than a chemical one? For when all is said and done, the accounts of love given to us by the modern biologists and psychologists are no more revealing than are the myths and legends about love told by the ancient Greeks. Indeed the latter are the more enlightening of the two for there can be no doubt that these old stories had deeper meanings than those lying on the surface of them. According to one old Greek myth the earth was once peopled by beings who were half man and half woman, composite creatures who grew so overbearing and arrogant that the gods on Mount Olympus became affronted and decided to punish them. So Zeus, father of all the gods, roused himself from sleep and first cleft the boastful mortals down the middle and then scattered the two separate halves widely over the face of the earth. As the result of this exceedingly severe punishment, one half of humanity has been searching for the other half from which it was torn in the hope of being able to re-unite with it and become complete again. The makers of this myth tell us that the yearning of humanity to recover its lost wholeness is the emotion which men call love.

The Greek account of love between the sexes has this advantage over the scientific, that it emphasizes a fact which is usually forgotten by the experts, namely that sexual love enters into and permeates every aspect of our emotional life. The so-called love experts, like all other specialists, make far too much of the small corner in which they happen to be interested, and are blind to everything happening elsewhere. For example, it has already been pointed out that the scientists regard love between the sexes as entirely subsidiary to the function of reproduction, sexual attraction being the bait by which Nature brings the man and woman together. But, as will be seen later in this book, love—and even love of a sexual nature—has a far wider field of action than this, so that we find writers declaring, and backing their declarations with sound arguments, that the real purpose of human love between the sexes is to assist the spiritual growth of the individual rather than to perpetuate the race. Berdyef strongly favours this view and writes of sexual love as follows: "The meaning and the purpose of the union between man and woman is to be found, not in the continuation of the species, or in its social import, but in personality, in its striving for the completeness of life and its longing for eternity". (*The Destiny of Man.*)

When doctors realize that they understand very little about a disease and its cause they abandon the effort to describe it and content themselves with making a catalogue of its symptoms and with calling the *ensemble* of symptoms a "syndrome". Having failed to give a convincing account of this curious syndrome love, a syndrome which was looked upon by the ancient Greeks as a kind of summer madness, we shall fall back on providing a list of its symptoms. I know of no better account of these symptoms than that given by the shepherd Silvius in Shakespeare's play *As You Like It*. It will be remembered that Phoebe asks him to say what being in love is like and he answers:

> It is to be made of sighs and tears.
> It is to be made of faith and service
> It is to be all made of fantasy,
> All made of passion, and all made of wishes,

> All adoration, duty and observance,
> All humbleness, all patience and impatience,
> All purity, all trial, all observance
> And so am I for Phoebe.

And since most of us have noted these symptoms in ourselves, perhaps once or twice or perchance many times, we can recall to mind our experiences and come to our own decisions as to the nature of love.

No form of human behaviour can ever be explained in terms of mind alone and this will become increasingly obvious in our further study of sexual love. We shall find that love between a man and a woman and between a woman and a man can be explained—in so far as it is explicable at all—only in terms of action and reaction between an individual and his physical and psychological environment. Love is a manifestation of an individual's sense of his own incompleteness and it can be said that the desire of a man for a woman, of a woman for a man and of both for children is the original source from which all forms of society have been derived. Sex-hunger is associated with a physical condition in which every sense organ of the body has been mobilized for the purpose of finding a person through whom this unsatisfied desire may be assuaged. In its essence therefore love is a compelling urge for contact and communication with another human being who will reveal her true nature to us and at the same time acts as the means by which our true nature is revealed to ourselves.

But it would be a serious error to regard sexuality as a separate and self-sufficient urge which moves within its own very limited boundaries. Love is the very reverse of this; it is an urge which has diffused far beyond its own erotic frontiers so that it colours the whole of our emotional life. So widely indeed has it spread that it would be difficult to name any sphere of activity which has not been affected by it. It has established particularly strong links with the creative work of the artist and also with that deep inner sense of the eternal and the divine which is the departure point for the great religions of this world. Freud realized how wide were the ramifications of sexuality when he described the "libido" as the driving force behind all human life. In his later writings he modified his original Libido Theory and recognized only two great drives or urges in the unconscious, namely *Eros* or the positive and creative drive of love and *Thanatos* or the destructive urge towards Death.

H. G. Wells places the several ingredients of love between a man and a woman and a woman and a man under the following headings:

"The recurrent craving for sexual completion.

"The lingering dependence of childhood, the need we feel to be 'mothered' or 'fathered'. We are lonely and to relieve our agoraphobia we want to nestle into someone protective.

"The craving for a dependent—the need to mother or father someone which will give us in return a sense of power.

"The craving for sympathy and imaginative response, the 'Persona-Shadow'. The craving, that is, for a friendly interested audience. The love-letters of many people are better than their love.

"The practical need for a loyal ally in all sorts of matters, for 'partnership without book-keeping', in which there is more than a mere give-and-take of services, in which there is an emotional tie.

"And ruling over all this tangle of motives is the strong irrational disposition, strengthened by tradition and usage, to concentrate the fulfilment of all these needs in one single possessed person of the opposite sex, who is '*my* man' or '*my* woman'. It is an exaggeration and misapplication of the natural mating instinct". (H. G. Wells, *The Anatomy of Frustration*, 1936.)

The belittling of sexual love so that it is looked upon as little more than a by-product of the act of reproduction is a very common error, and it is not only the materialists and scientists who are guilty of it. It is a fault which many moralists have committed. They look upon sexual love with strong disfavour and regard it as a rather indecorous and crude method of securing the continuation of the human race. In the bottom of their hearts they regret that a better and more spiritual means was not devised for this, but since it was the Creator who was responsible for selecting the method it has perforce to be accepted. They admit therefore love between the sexes to the world but only on sufferance and carefully hedged about with innumerable rules and regulations. Yet, as has already been said, love between the sexes extends far beyond the confines of the reproductive act, and at its best it can attain the same high level as a religious or aesthetic experience. In the opinion of the Russian philosopher Ouspensky, the sexual act provides the ordinary man or woman with the nearest approach to a mystical experience that they are ever likely to get. "Of all we know in life" he writes, "only in love is there a taste of the mystical, a taste of ecstasy. Nothing else in our life brings us so near to the limit of human possibilities beyond which begins the unknown and in this lies, without doubt, the chief cause of the terrible power of sex over human souls." P. D. Ouspensky (*A New Model of the Universe*).

The Hindus and the Moslems also hold this view that the love of a man for a woman and of a woman for a man provides ordinary people with a foretaste of that highest love of all, known only to the saints, the love of God. For this reason the Deity in Moslem literature is often referred to as the Beloved One. There is also the suggestion in Eastern sacred literature that a man acquires the highest form of love—the love of God—by graduating first in the lower two classes. First

he must learn love for a woman at its best, then he learns how
to love his fellow men, and to accept them as his brothers, and
finally he may attain the highest love of all—the love of the
Divine.

The Greeks, from whom we have derived much of our culture, had a less exalted view of sexual love than the Oriental.
They looked upon the love of a man for a woman as a kind of
sporadic madness which might suddenly afflict even the sanest
of men and render him irresponsible for his actions. In order to
emphasize the blindness and the accidental nature of sexual
attraction, they used as a symbol of it the mischievous shooting
of that blind-folded boy, Cupid. And the Greeks were quite
right in laying stress on the haphazard methods of the emotion
known to us as "falling in love". Plato writes of this particular
variety of love in his Symposium, describing it as the realization of, and the delight in beauty and there can be no doubt that
those who fall in love have entered a new world of dazzling
loveliness. To lovers the sky is bluer than it formerly was, the
scent of the flowers more fragrant, colours and forms more
exquisite than anything which they had experienced before.
Yes, to fall in love is to pass through a gateway into a new and
ecstatically beautiful world.

The word "falling" has been well chosen, for the onset of
sexual love is often extraordinarily abrupt and as unexpected as
most falls are. Walter de la Mare gives an excellent description of
that sudden attraction known as "love at first sight". He writes
of it as follows: "Whatever preparation in the body and mind,
unperceived by ourselves, has been made for its reception,
Love waits for no man. He neither knocks nor is announced.
We fall in love and in so doing soar, for the time being at
least, into an earthly paradise. No more than a turn of the head
or the accents of a voice may have been the decoy. There may
be no tinge of desire, no immediate hint or shadow of any

appeal for recognition. In a moment we have staked our one and only bright penny and have lost; and in so doing have won a hitherto unrealized self. Whatever may follow this invasion, the surrender has been mute, without terms of reflection." (Walter de la Mare. *Love*. Faber & Faber.)

Yes, when we fall in love we fall precipitately into an entirely new world. But will its vivid colours, its sweet scents and its enchanting forms of loveliness last? Here is an important question but it is a question which few of those who find themselves in this garden of delight ask themselves. Nor can they be expected to be thinking of the future when all that is so wonderful is with them in the here and now.

Yet strange as it may seem to some people, romantic love in the choosing of life partners is comparatively new in human history. It has not always been regarded as a necessary or even as a desirable basis for marriage, and there are many countries in which the older view still prevails, the view that romantic love is of a butterfly mating and is too delicate and evanescent a thing to withstand the jolts and shocks of married life. In these old-fashioned countries it is believed that marriage has to be built on foundations much more secure and much more lasting than the fantasies of those who have "fallen in love". And, as will be seen in another chapter, in such countries, instead of leaving the choice of partners entirely in the hands of young and entirely inexperienced people, the parents still retain responsibility for the choice of wives and husbands for their children.

Romantic love came into vogue in the Middle Ages and its essential characteristic was that it looked upon the beloved object as something very precious and very difficult to possess. At first, love of this kind was not directed towards women with whom the lovers could ever hope to have a sexual relationship, but towards women who were separated from them by insuperable social and moral barriers. According to Bertrand

Russell, the Church had performed so thoroughly its "task of making men feel that sex was inherently impure, that it had become impossible to feel any poetic sentiment towards a lady unless she was regarded as unattainable. Accordingly love, if it was to have any beauty, had to be platonic." (Bertrand Russell, *Marriage and Morals*. George Allen & Unwin.)

It was of this kind of love that troubadours sang and to it that the knights plighted their troth as they rode into the lists carrying on their person a lady's glove as an emblem of the fair and unattainable loved one.

At the Renaissance and as a result of the movement it produced away from the hitherto all-powerful Church and in the direction of paganism, love became a little less platonic in character. But it still remained poetic and the best account of romantic love at this stage of its history is that given by Cervantes in his description of Don Quixote's love for Dulcinea. Romantic love may be said to have reached its zenith in this country during the last century in the age of Shelley and Byron. When Shelley fell in love he was filled with exquisite emotions which found a ready outlet in his poetry, and because, in his capacity of poet, he regarded these fruits of love as entirely good, he saw no reason for putting any restraint on falling in love. By Shelley's time the barriers between the lover and his beloved had been lowered so that they were far less formidable than they had been in the days of the knights and the troubadours. With courage and determination all obstacles could be overcome, and this added zest and still more poetry to the final triumph of the lovers.

It is interesting to re-read the novels and plays written in the latter half of the last century in the light of all this, for many of them are concerned with the change-over taking place from the older marriage by family arrangement to the much newer and more romantic notion of marriage for love. These old works give an excellent description of the conflict between the older generation which was still insisting on the need for good judgement and discrimination in the choosing of a husband or a wife, and the younger generation which was going all out for the new idea of a romantic marriage.

As is usual in disputes of this kind, truth lay on both sides. The older generation had placed far too much emphasis on social and economic advantages, whilst the younger generation was swinging over too violently in the direction of romantic love, oblivious of the fact, as are many younger people of the present time, that success in marriage entails something more comprehensive and more lasting than delight in each other's appearance and company. But although romantic love and poetry alone are unable to ensure a happy and successful marriage, they are highly desirable ingredients of a marriage. After giving an excellent account of the advent of romantic love in Europe, Bertrand Russell sums up his own personal feelings on this subject as follows: "I believe myself that romantic love is the source of the most intense delights that life can offer. In the relation of a man and a woman who love each other with passion and imagination and tenderness there is something of inestimable value, to be ignorant of which is a great misfortune to any human being."

The finest account of love of which I have any knowledge is that of A. R. Orage, one-time editor of *The New Age*, whose description of the three kinds of love is of such outstanding merit that I am compelled to quote from it.

"You must learn", he begins, "to distinguish amongst at least three kinds of love (though there are seven in all); instinctive love, emotional love and conscious love. There is not much fear you cannot learn the first two, but the third is rare and depends on effort as well as intelligence. Instinctive love has chemistry as its base. All biology is chemistry, or perhaps we should say alchemistry; and the affinities of instinctive love, manifesting in the attractions, repulsions, mechanical and chemical combinations we call love, courtship, marriage, children and family, are only the human equivalents of a chemist's laboratory. . . . Instinctive love being chemical is as strong, and lasts as long as the substances and qualities of which it is the manifestation.

"Emotional love is not rooted in biology. It is, in fact, as often anti-biological in its character and direction. Instinctive love obeys the laws of biology, that is to say chemistry, and proceeds by affinities. But emotional love is often the mutual attraction of disaffinities and biological incongruities. Emotional love is not only short-lived, but evokes the slayer. Such love creates hate in its object, if hatred is not already there . . . These are the tragedies of love emotional.

"Conscious love rarely obtains between humans; but it can be illustrated in the relations of a man to his favourites in the animal and vegetable kingdoms. The development of the horse and the dog from their original state of nature; the cultivation of flowers and fruit—these are examples of a primitive form of conscious love, primitive because the motive is still egoistic and utilitarian. . . . The conscious love motive, in its developed state, is the wish that the object should arrive at its own native perfections, regardless of the consequences to the lover. 'So she become perfectly herself, what matter I' says the conscious lover. 'I will go to hell, if only she may go to heaven.' And the paradox is that such love always evokes a similar attitude in its object. Conscious love begets conscious love. It is rare amongst human beings because, in the first place, the vast majority are children who look to be loved but not to love; secondly because perfection is seldom conceived as the proper end of human love—though it alone distinguishes adult human love from infantile and animal love; thirdly because humans do not know, even if they wish, what is good for those they love; and fourthly, because it never occurs by chance, but must be the subject of resolve, effort, self-conscious choice. As little as Bushido or the Order of Chivalry grew up accidentally does conscious love arise by nature". (*Selected Essays and Critical Writings* of A. R. Orage, 1935 London, Stanley Nott Ltd.).

What should be regarded then as being the right motive for marrying? This is a question that admits of no short reply for, as Walter de la Mare attests in his book, *Love*, there may be many different reasons for marrying: "There are marriages of convenience; marriages intent on an heir, a housekeeper or a home; on comfort or companionship; the outcome of pique or mere caprice". All these, and romantic love as well, may end in the celebration of a wedding. In the Church service for the Solemnization of Matrimony, five solemn declarations are made and two supreme promises exchanged; one of the latter is to love and cherish and the other is to love, honour and obey. The promise on the part of the bride to obey is now considered one-sided and humiliating and is more often than not omitted from the service.

But the ingredients in a marriage, the conditions which go to make a success of it and the deficiencies which are likely to bring about its failure, are subjects of such supreme importance that they will have to be discussed more fully later in this book.

2

MARRIAGE

DURING the last fifty years many old customs and institutions have been critically surveyed, pronounced out-of-date and swept aside to make room for others more in harmony with the times. Other ancient ordinances and practices have been attacked but have managed to survive, and amongst these is the institution of marriage. There have, of course, always been people of the opinion that marriage was a quite unnecessary formality which served little or no purpose and should therefore be abolished. If a man and woman chose to live together for a time, it was entirely their own affair.

This critical attitude to marriage is far from being a modern one, and it was particularly common amongst the intellectuals of the late eighteenth and early nineteenth centuries. That great advocate of romantic love, the poet Shelley, felt very strongly on the point and he wrote:

> I never was attached to that great sect
> Whose doctrine is that each one should select
> Out of the crowd a mistress or a friend
> And all the rest, though wise and good, commend
> To cold oblivion; though it is the code
> Of modern morals, and the beaten road
> Which those poor slaves with weary footsteps tread
> Who travel to their home among the dead
> By the broad highway of the world, and so—
> With one chain'd friend, perhaps a jealous foe
> The dreariest and the longest journey go.

Now Shelley was no libertine but an idealist and ardent social reformer. He genuinely felt that marriage was confining to the human spirit and that as it served no useful purpose it should be given up by all enlightened people. Like many other critics of marriage he regarded it as an artificial product of modern civilization, but in thinking thus he was entirely wrong in his facts. Marriage is far more than an artificial device for it can be justified on biological and psychological grounds as is clearly shown by a study of animal behaviour.

But first of all it must be made clear that marriage was not instituted primarily for the purpose of regulating the sexual behaviour of a man and a woman, but for the sake of the family resulting from their union. In all parts of the world, and at all times, marriage has been looked upon as being a preliminary step to the formation of a new family and amongst many peoples, both primitive and civilized, a marriage which does not lead to parenthood is regarded as being a failure. In some countries this feeling that a marriage without children is meaningless is so strong that sterility or impotence are accepted as grounds for its annulment.

Biologically speaking, five stages can be recognized in the production and rearing of the offspring of mammals. The first stage of this process is the development of the sex urge in the male and the female, the second stage their courtship, the third mating, the fourth pregnancy and the fifth parenthood. It is obvious that each stage in this process leads inevitably towards the stage which follows it, but it should be noted that in the great majority of the higher mammals the sex urge is not continuous, as it is in human beings, but rhythmic. Because of its periodicity, and because also of the rapidity with which the young mature, there is far less need amongst animals for the relationship between the parents to be permanent. Yet, the same parents often remain together during several breeding seasons.

The most striking difference between human beings and animals is that the human young remain for a very much longer time dependent on their parents than do the young of the animals. It may be said indeed that the duties of the human parents begin nine months before the birth of the child and continue, in Western countries, until the child gains adulthood, which is to say some eighteen years later. It also has to be born in mind that man has been successful in his struggle for survival chiefly by virtue of his ability to adapt the environment to his needs, and that the knowledge which enables him to do this has to be handed on from one generation to another. This means that the human young have not only to be fed, clothed and housed by their parents, but also to be educated by them. Because of this the man and woman have to remain together until their children have been taught all that it is necessary for them to know in order to make a living, and this sometimes means that the children have to remain on their hands until they are in their late twenties. All these parental duties make it necessary for the union of the man and the woman to continue, not only until the youngest members of the family are fully developed physically, but also until they have attained economic and cultural maturity. In this country and at the present day, this may mean that the responsibilities of the parents may not end until the children are nearer thirty than twenty.

In order that the interests of the children may be secured a legal contract is entered into by the man and the woman, and in many countries this is done in the presence of the community of which they are members. This legal contract lays on the two parties certain definite obligations, both towards each other and towards their future offspring. Religious sanctions of marriage are less widely spread, and the chief reason for resorting to them is that they are held to be of a much more binding nature than the legal ones. Whereas a defaulter is always able to fly to the ends of the earth in order to escape from the rules and regulations in which his fellow men have enmeshed him, he is unable to escape from his religious obligations, for the eye of Heaven follows him wherever he goes. Religious sanctions were therefore introduced to support marriage by means of religious fears, and up till recently they have served these purposes very efficiently. Since the decline of religion their efficiency has become much less.

Some anthropologists and experts in economics and sociology have argued that as the State has to a large extent taken over the cares and responsibilities of the father—for example, the work of protecting the family from assault—it can equally take over some of the duties of the mother, thus separating the two functions of child-bearing and child-nurture. But those who have suggested this have forgotten how manifold are the duties of parents towards their children, and they have also overlooked the important fact that no child who has been emotionally starved is likely to grow up into a well-balanced and effective citizen. They have also failed to give sufficient weight, not only to the fact that a State is unable to supply a child with emotional nourishment, but also that there exists a strong parental urge in the great majority of mothers and in quite a large number of fathers, an urge which cannot be pushed arbitrarily aside.

History shows that marriage is an institution which has always existed and it is unlikely that humanity will ever be able to get on without it. Contrary to what is often stated, there has never been a time in human history when complete promiscuity existed between men and woman. However primitive the culture there have always been certain rules and regulations to determine with which woman in the community a man was entitled to have sexual intercourse and under what conditions it could take place. Thus, nowhere in the world has it ever been

31

legal for such intercourse to occur between father and daughter, mother and son or brother and sister. It is quite true that in the royal families of ancient Egypt, Peru and Hawai, a marriage between a brother and a sister was considered correct, but this cannot be taken as an exception to this general law against incest, for the status of the ruling monarchs in all these countries was exceptional. They were looked upon as being gods and the fact that the royal family was exempt from this law of incest was regarded as proof of their divine nature.

The law against incest is universal and the reason for its existence is very clear. At all costs the disintegration of the family unit has to be avoided, and since the intrusion of sexual interest into the home might have a disruptive action on the family, it has to be sternly forbidden. The very fact that this taboo is, and always has been, universal is sufficient to prove how widely the value of the family has been recognized. Consequently those who attack the institution of marriage are not the gallant pioneers they fondly imagine themselves to be, but should be looked upon as being reactionaries who are unwittingly trying to destroy an institution which men and women have found by long experience to be essential to their welfare.

But because marriage and the family are ancient and widespread institutions based on thoroughly sound biological and anthropological principles, they should not necessarily be regarded as rigid and immutable elements in human life. Nothing in Nature or in human affairs is immutable and it is quite possible that certain changes will have to be made in that so old and honoured institution known as marriage. A nation resembles an individual in that it is sometimes forced to adapt itself to its environment, and should our national environment undergo a still greater change in the future than it has undergone during the last half century, it is possible that some change in the outward form of marriage will have to be made. Some environmental changes, such as the emancipation and education of women, have already had their effect on marriage, and this will be discussed in the later chapters of this book. Should a time arrive when it becomes necessary to modify the external forms and trappings of marriage and the family, it is to be hoped that those responsible for the alterations will keep clear in their minds what is vital in these institutions and what are only their cultural dressings.

The crisis through which the institution of marriage is at present passing is only a part of that much bigger crisis taking place in human affairs, the upshot of which nobody can foretell. The world is divided into two great camps, one formed by those who believe that the State exists for the benefit and the protection of the individual, and the other which holds the contrary view that the individual exists for the benefit of the State, and much will depend on which of these two opinions finally prevails. If the Christian values on which all our Western culture is based are abandoned, then the fate of marriage and of the family is sealed, for the one cannot survive without the other. Should the views of those who believe that the individual exists for the sake of the State, as the bee exists for the sake of the hive, and the ant for the sake of the ant heap, then marriage and the family must go by the board, for in beehives and ant heaps such things are anomalies. In the brave new world of the communistic type, the rearing of young will be handed over to the State and a prolonged association between a man and a woman will be unnecessary. Not only will love between one man and one woman be superfluous, but it will also be against the interests of the State. Love is an unruly emotion which is likely to divert the worker's attention from his duties to the community, so love as well as marriage will have to be banished from the human ant-heap of the future.

Up till now marriage has been regarded only as an institution for safeguarding the interests of the children, but this is not necessarily the sole motive for two people getting married. Marriage confers certain advantages on the contracting parties, and in some societies it is eagerly desired by young men and women as a sign that they have attained full maturity. Only after a man has married is he recognized in some tribes as being his own master, a state of independence which is rendered still more complete by the birth of his first child. The change wrought in the status of the woman by marriage is even greater. It is true that her husband now exercises authority over her but her subservience to him is much less than was her former sub-servience to her parents.

There are different varieties of marriage but the most widely spread at the present day, the most ancient and the most bio-logical variety, is monogamous marriage. As has previously been said, some animals retain the same mates for several breed-ing seasons, and even for life, and this is particularly true of man's nearest relatives, the anthropoid apes. There is evidence also that monogamy exists amongst the lowest races of man, the aborigines of Australia being monogamous as were also the now extinct aborigines of Tasmania.

In those countries in which polygamous marriages are cus-tomary, the motive for them is economic and social rather than sexual. A man does not acquire new wives so much because he wants novelty, as because he is a rich man and wishes to dis-play to the world his wealth. A large number of wives is there-fore a privilege—if privilege it be—which is restricted to men of the wealthier classes. Another possible incentive to acquiring a large number of wives is that they will be able to work for their husband and to produce children who will also work for him on reaching a mature age. King Solomon possessed as many as seven hundred wives and three hundred concubines, but according to Westermarck, he was completely outshone by a certain King of Loango, whose harem reached the fantastic number of seven thousand. But the point to remember is that no matter how numerous are a man's wives, each wife represents a separate marriage contract entered into by him with regard to that particular woman. The polygamous family therefore consists of a cluster of families radiating out from a common centre in the person of one husband and father.

Polyandry, or the marriage of a woman to several men, is much less common and it is practised principally in Tibet and amongst the Todas of India. It happens quite naturally that a group of brothers or of cousins comes together and arranges to have certain properties and either one or more wives in common. Access to the said wife or wives is regulated by definite rules, and should a child be born it is immediately allotted to one or other member of the group who is henceforth recognized by all as its father. The polyandrous is the obverse of the polygamous family, that is to say it can be resolved into a collection of families radiating out from a common centre in the person of a single wife and mother or of two or three wives and mothers.

Philosophers, wits, poets and dramatists have expressed a great variety of views on the fecund subject of marriage, some of them in the form of epigrams, others as admonitions to the young and yet others in terms of pure comedy. I owe the great majority of the following quotations to Sir Adolphe Abrahams's small book, *Woman: Man's Equal:*

"A good marriage would be between a blind wife and a deaf husband". *Montaigne.*

"He was reputed a wise man that made answer to the question—'When should a man marry?'—'A young man not yet, an elder man, not at all'." *Francis Bacon.*

"Marriage is a step so grave and decisive that it attracts light-hearted, variable men by its very awfulness". *Churton Collins.*

35

"He that hath wife and children hath given hostages to fortune for they are impediments to great enterprises, either of virtue or of mischief". *Francis Bacon.*

"Whether to marry or not to marry? Whichever you do you will repent". *Socrates.*

"Every woman should marry, and no man". *Disraeli.*

"There is one fool at least to every married couple." *Henry Fielding.*

An old writer on marriage, Jacobus de Voragine, gives the following arguments for and against marriage:

"1. Hast thou means? thou hast one to keep and increase it. 2. Hast none? thou hast one to help get it. 3. Art in prosperity? thine happiness is doubled. 4. Art in adversity? she'll comfort, assist, bear a part of thy burden to make it more tolerable. 5. Art at home? she'll drive away melancholy. 6. Art abroad? she looks after thee going from home, wishes for thee in thine absence, and joyfully welcomes thy return. 7. There's nothing delightsome without society, no society so sweet as matrimony. 8. The band of conjugal love is adamantine. 9. The sweet company of kinsmen increaseth, the number of parents is doubled, of brothers, sisters, nephews. 10. Thou art made a father by a fair and happy issue. 11. Moses curseth the barrenness of matrimony, how much more a single life? 12. If nature escape not punishment, surely thy will shall not avoid it.

"All this is true, say you, and who knows it not? but how easy a matter is it to answer these motives, and to make an *Antiparodia* quite opposite unto it? To exercise myself I will essay:

"1. Hast thou means? thou hast one to spend it. 2. Hast none? thy beggary is increased. 3. Art in prosperity? thy happiness is ended. 4. Art in adversity? like Job's wife she'll aggravate thy misery, vex thy soul, make thy burden intolerable. 5. Art at home? she'll scold thee out of doors. 6. Art abroad? If thou be wise, keep thee so, she'll perhaps graft horns in thy absence, scowl on thee coming home. 7. Nothing gives more content than solitariness, no solitariness like this of a single life. 8. The band of marriage is adamantine, no hope of loosing it, thou art undone. 9. Thy number increaseth, thou shalt be devoured by thy wife's friends. 10. Thou art made a cornuto by an unchaste wife, and shalt bring up other folk's children, instead of thine own. 11. Paul commends marriage, yet he prefers a single life. 12. Is marriage honourable? What an immortal crown belongs to virginity!

'Tis a hazard both ways I confess, to live single or to marry, it may be bad, it may be good, as it is a cross and calamity on the one side, so 'tis a sweet delight, an incomparable happiness, a most unspeakable benefit, a sole content, on the other, 'tis all in the proof. Be not then so wayward, so covetous, so distrustful, so curious and nice, but let's all marry.... "Take me to thee, and thee to me", to-morrow is St. Valentine's day, let's keep it holiday for Cupid's sake, for that great god Love's sake, for Hymen's sake, and celebrate Venus's vigil with our ancestors for company together, singing as they did ...

> Let those love now who never loved before,
> And those who always loved now love the more,
> Sweet loves are born with every opening spring;
> Birds from the tender boughs their pledges sing, etc. . .

As has already been said, the fact that marriage is an institution which is at present indispensable to our culture does not necessarily mean that its outward forms and trappings can never be changed. Our cultural environment is continually altering and with these changes some modification of customs and national institutions may have to be effected.

There are those who recommend that two types of marriage contract should be made available to people, a more permanent type of contract supported by religious sanctions and celebrated in church, and a less binding and permanent contract of a purely secular nature which could be followed in a few years time by the religious type of marriage if the contracting parties so desired it. The former type of contract would provide a far more satisfactory apprenticeship to marriage than the so-called "trial marriages" suggested some years ago by Judge Lindsay.

It should also be recognized that there are people who by temperament, by profession, or by both, are entirely unsuited to marriage and who would be well advised to leave it severely alone. Saints and men and women who have dedicated their lives to some great social work or enterprise are amongst such people, and so also are great creative artists and cinema stars. Rudolph Valentino, who is the very symbol of the modern world's conception of "romantic love", himself held this view. Havelock Ellis tells us that he is reported to have exclaimed on his death-bed that he had "lived in hell" and that "Fate mocked artists". It would certainly be better if those light-hearted contractors of short-term marriages at Hollywood were to reduce the work of the already overburdened American divorce courts, either by avoiding marriage altogether or else by devising some private form of renewable marriage contract. It would make life easier for them and would at the same time add to the dignity of an institution which it is necessary for us to retain, the institution of marriage.

Marriage is still required and for two main reasons; it is necessary in the interests of the children; it is necessary for the security of women in general, even although the security it may offer them is a very limited one. But though marriage has to be retained it has at the same time to be recognized that much suffering occurs both *in* and *through* marriage. We have only to look at the steep rise in the divorce rate in the West to realize how often marriage turns out to be a painful failure.

And it is a failure for a great many different reasons, or it would be more correct to say for a great many and different aggregates of reasons, all working against it at the same time. What is noticeable is that the reasons for a husband and wife either parting from each other or else living together in mutual misery are seldom of a dramatic or startling quality. More often than not the conjugal trouble is the result of humdrum forms of irritation or an acute boredom, and more particularly boredom on the part of the wife. Dr. Van de Velde quotes Dr. Caesare Lombroro, on this subject. She is a medical woman with two children and she writes of her own marriage experiences as follows:

She writes: "The loneliness of mind and heart to which a man can condemn his wife is much more painful and injurious than tyranny and violent brutality, which public opinion so reprobates. For these ills are visible, grossly corporeal and often only temporary, for the reaction of public opinion which they immediately provoke offers in itself some protection and remedy. But the loneliness of desertion is an invisible, unimaginable anguish which in itself makes resistance vain, and poisons every hour of the day, and all the days of an unhappy life, for it is the *negation* of life and hope and the discouragement, the disintegration of purpose it produces, which becomes more unendurable than any swift and violent pain".

The security and success of a marriage depend on a great many things and particularly on the four following factors (1) a reasonably good choice of partners to start with; (2) a satisfactory attitude of the two people concerned both to each other and to the world in general; (3) a satisfactory solution of the various problems connected with the planning of a family; (4) a reasonably satisfactory and harmonious sexual life of the two partners together. Some writers would place these requirements in a different order and some would, quite rightly, add to the above list, the possession of sound health by both of the partners. In the following chapter the requirements for success in marriage will be examined in turn and the first to be dealt with will be a reasonably good choice of partners. When we come to investigate this all-important requisite for a successful marriage, we shall find that, far from exercising judgement and discrimination in the choice of partners, the majority of Western people blunder into marriage blindly and without any thought for the morrow. Some of these blunderers turn out to be lucky but the great majority are unlucky.

3

COURTSHIP

HAVING discussed love and marriage and their relationship, and having agreed that marriage provided a necessary background to enduring love and that love was in turn a desirable component of marriage, we can now go back in time and discuss that preliminary to love and marriage, namely, courtship.

Courtship is common both to man and to the animals and it is the means by which they both select their partners in marriage. And courting, more especially amongst the birds, has many resemblances to the same activity in human beings. Birds have a great sense of rhythm and posture and the dances of some birds are as formal and as graceful as an old-fashioned gavotte. Moreover, courting in the bird world would seem to be regulated by certain rules and conventions. N. J. Berrill states that it is customary for cock birds to compete for hens by displaying themselves in their own territories rather than by staging a free-for-all rush upon the hens. And when a cock postures and sings within its own territory it is not only advertising its charms to any females in that neighbourhood, but is at the same time warning members of its own sex not to come too near. (N. J. Berrill, F.R.S. *Sex and the Nature of Things.* Gollancz, 1954).

But there is this great difference between the courtship of man and that of the animals that whereas man is able to effect courtship and sexual union all the year round, breeding for most animals is a rhythmic activity which takes place only

41

during the "rutting" season. The red deer living in the Scottish Highlands provide a good example of the rhythmic character of courtship and breeding. For the greater part of the year the deer of both sexes are in a non-sexual state and during this time they live in separate herds, the male herd under the domination of a stag, and the female herd following the lead of an old female. In the autumn, as the "rutting" season approaches, the herds of males break up and the individual stags move off to found harems of does for themselves and, having established these, they guard them zealously. But throughout the whole of the "rutting" season the herds of does still keep together, and with regard to everything except love-making they remain as before, under the control of their female leaders.

Monkeys and apes approach nearest to man in their breeding arrangements. The males remain sexually active all the year round, whilst the females, although they show definite cycles of sexual activity, are willing to receive the males almost at any time.

The great majority of birds breed only once a year and most frequently in the spring whenever the weather is propitious and food becomes more plentiful. The farther north we travel in the northern hemisphere and the farther south we go in the southern hemisphere the later becomes the breeding season. For light plays a large part in the chain of events which leads to the awakening of sexual activity, as is shown by the fact that the breeding season can be hastened by subjecting birds in any region to the action of artificial sunlight.

It is, of course, of the utmost importance to the young of mammals and birds in a state of nature that they should not enter the world until the environment gives them a reasonably good chance of surviving, and it is this which is responsible for the restriction of the breeding season. But for domesticated animals, fed and cared for by man, this question of a propitious environment does not arise so that they are able to breed all the year round, provided, of course, that the female is "on heat".

Courtship is not only the means by which partners are chosen and wooed, but it is also a stimulant to sexual excitement and the prelude to sexual union. Through the stimulating action of the messages received through the special senses, the male and female are both brought into a state of sexual activity, and since much that applies to animals applies also to human beings, it will be of interest to review the parts played by each of these special senses in this process of evoking sexual desire.

Touch is the most primitive of all our special senses and it is also the sense which is most stimulating to sexual excitement and activity. Touch leads more directly than any other sense to the desired goal, and because of its immediate action on sexuality, it has the biggest place in courtship. Amongst such lowly creatures as insects and crabs, tactile sensation plays so dominant a role in all their activities that it would appear to be the only sense involved in courtship. But even when we leave these low levels and observe higher forms of life we find that touch is still taking a leading part in courtship. Newman, who spent many hours watching wild elephants during the breeding season, describes the skilful way in which the bull elephant uses his trunk in courting, crossing it with the trunk of the cow elephant and even putting the tip of it into her mouth. It would be true to say, therefore, that the elephant makes use of that natural and time-honoured human overture to love, the kiss.

Kissing has been brought to a fine art by lovers, and in erotic literature many different forms of kissing are described. In many of these variations of kissing great use is made of the tongue, and this means that taste is brought into action as well as smell and touch. Hence the description given in classical literature of Poppaea's kisses, that they possessed "the flavour of wild berries". Fashions of kissing differ in different countries, and it is well-known that Mongolians rub their noses together instead of making use of their lips and their tongues.

It is interesting that hugging and kissing become a passion to many girls about the time of puberty, even although these actions have not as yet acquired any real sexual significance. Ticklishness is also a subject of interest to sexologists, and that tickling is not very far removed from love-making is revealed by the fact that, in certain races, to tickle is regarded as tantamount to making love. It is also recorded that Catherine II of Russia appointed official court ticklers, whose duty it was to tickle her Imperial feet at the same time that they were recounting to her ribald stories, or singing to her wanton songs.

The sense of smell is so highly developed in mammals that during the breeding season its importance is secondary only to the sense of touch. We have only to take a dog for a country walk to realize how many and how rich are the impressions which it receives through the nose. So important is smell to some animals that the olfactory lobes of their brains, that is to say, the parts of their brains which are concerned with the registration of smell, are bulkier than are their cerebral hemispheres. It is not surprising, therefore, that smell enters very largely into the courtship of mammals.

Amongst men and the higher apes smell is of much less importance, but it is an interesting fact that in man smell has very strong links with the emotions. For example, the scent of a rose can suddenly bring back to us memories of something which happened many years ago, and may revive for us some scene so vividly that it is not so much remembered by us as relived. Because of this highly emotional quality of smell it has a more important place in courtship than it would otherwise have.

At a very early era in history women were clever enough to realize the existence of this strong emotional content in smell, and in all countries and at all times women have made great use of artificial scents and perfumes. It is, of course, quite possible that some women have done this as much for their own pleasure as for the purpose of attracting men, for it has been shown that women are far more sensitive to scents and perfumes than are men. But that these commodities have for the feminine sex a sexual as well as an aesthetic significance is strongly suggested by the fact that sensitivity to smell is noticeably increased in girls after puberty. Our legislators in the eighteenth century evidently favoured the view that perfumes were being deliberately used by women for the purpose of ensnaring men, for a special Act of Parliament was passed in the year 1770 to the following effect: "That all women of whatever age, rank, profession or degree, whether virgin maid or widow, that shall from and after such an Act impose upon, seduce and betray into matrimony any of His Majesty's subjects by reason of scents, paints, cosmetics, washes, artificial teeth, false hair, Spanish wool, iron stays, hoops, high-heeled shoes or bolstered hips shall incur the penalty of the law now in force against witchcraft and like misdemeanours, and that the marriage upon conviction shall stand null and void." (Quoted by Mrs. G. F. Lyell in *The Magic of Herbs*.) Whether or not this Act is still on the Statute Book I do not know, but if it is a great many marriages at the present day are capable of being declared null and void. It takes more than a law against witchcraft to separate the fair sex from its perfumes.

Sound also takes part in the activity of courtship, and the Swedish philosopher, Sperbe, has declared that if human speech were to be traced back to its earliest beginnings, it would be found to have sprung from two primitive human cries, the call of a hungry child for its mother and of a man to his mate. Sound also enters largely into the courtship of animals and it is only during the breeding season that the voice of the male attains its fullest power and range. This sudden development of the male voice is particularly noticeable amongst birds. It is of course true that of late years ornithologists have been inclined to attribute the singing of the cock bird in spring time to other things than a desire to attract the hen, to such motives, for example, as the proclamation of his own proprietary rights over some particular locality, or merely to exuberance of spirits. But surely this is insufficient of itself to explain these sudden outbursts of singing which advertise the arrival of the mating season in our English woods, and since it is the cock bird alone who makes all this noise, may we not assume that the hen bird has become specially responsive to song about this time. It is noteworthy also that it is only in the male that the quality of the voice changes at puberty, and to my way of thinking this strongly suggested that this deepening of his voice has for the female a strong sexual significance.

Nor is it only amongst birds that the voice of the male plays this prominent role in courtship. The old troubadours of the Middle Ages and their less romantic but highly popular successors of today, the American crooners, are other examples of the part played by sound in the evocation of love. And that music in all its forms is the true food of love was noted long ago by that very acute observer, William Shakespeare.

Sight has been left to the last for consideration, even though sight is by far the most valuable of our special senses, and the sense which dominates all others in the human being. An examination of the part played by vision in arousing sexual desire brings us straight up against the riddle of aesthetics, so that we have to answer this question: "Are our ideals of female or of male beauty based on some general aesthetic principle, or is the whole philosophy of aesthetics derived from our sexual feelings?" In other words, does sexuality evoke in us a sense of beauty, or is it the other way round?

To discuss this riddle of aesthetics fully would take us too far from the theme of this book, and all that it is possible to say here is that the sexual and the non-sexual factors in our appreciation of beauty are so closely interwoven that it is quite impossible to separate them. This being so, we can substitute for the former question this smaller one: "What is feminine beauty?" The first comment to be made on it is that ideals of feminine beauty, like other ideals, are subject to the swing of fashion, so that what was acclaimed beautiful in one century and in one country, is regarded as sexually unattractive in another century and in another country. For example, the voluptuous and exuberant type of woman portrayed by Rubens is no longer looked upon with widespread favour in many countries at the present day, but has had to yield place to a different ideal, namely that of the rather immature and boyish type of woman. But this does not mean that the Rubens woman is nowadays at a discount everywhere, for in Moslem lands generous curves, luscious features and fatness are still highly favoured.

It would probably be true to say that in every country the man and woman who best represents the characteristics of the people inhabiting that land is regarded with the greatest favour. This idea is supported by the fact that it is quite usual for the men and women living there to take special pains to accentuate in themselves, by artificial means, the natural characteristics of their race. Breadth of shoulder is one of the cherished features of the American male, and breadth of shoulder is accentuated artificially in the States by the use of extra folds of shoulder padding. Eastern women are usually the possessors of very large and lustrous eyes, and they go to the trouble of accentuating by art these natural features of theirs. Even the hairy Ainus, the most hirsute of all races, deliberately call attention to their national shagginess, whether they be males or not.

Grace of movement must also be taken into account in any assessment of beauty, and a woman who is deficient in static loveliness may often compensate for what she lacks by the beauty of her movements. How a woman holds herself, how she crosses a room, the way in which she sits, her way of rising and moving, are of far greater importance than a great many women appreciate, for these are qualities to which too little attention is paid by the women of today. This is particularly true of the English-speaking countries, and above all of America. Beautifully coiffured, splendidly furred, expensively gowned and skilfully made-up, the American woman is liable to fall to pieces immediately she starts to move. Grace of movement has always counted for much amongst males and in the East it still counts for much amongst them. It was not without good reason that the mothers of a hundred years ago sent their daughters to classes in deportment where they were taught how to hold themselves and how to move. The untutored Eastern peasant and the African negress carries herself and moves with a natural grace which the English-speaking Western woman would do well to imitate.

It would probably be true to say that the man's conception of feminine beauty is much more highly standardized than is the female's conception of beauty in the man. This is all to the good that the woman should subscribe to a wider range of beauty than the man since she is usually given less choice in the selection of a marriage partner than is the male. For the woman, strength of muscle and of character are usually of greater importance than an Adonis-like type of masculine beauty, a fact which accounts for the successes which many physically unattractive men have with the opposite sex. Both cleverness and brute strength appeal to the female, although neither of these qualities in themselves ensure that their possessor will make a satisfactory husband. A cleverness which amounts to genius would seem to be a drawback so far as marriage is concerned, for geniuses are notoriously difficult to live with. Kretschner tells us that when the King of Sweden attended the funeral of a certain Swedish genius and expressed his sympathy to the widow, the bereft lady answered him quite simply: "Sir, he was intolerable to live with". If the wives of other geniuses were equally honest and outspoken, the immense disadvantages attached to being married to a genius would be better known.

Not that a bad reputation in the matrimonial market is likely to prevent a brilliantly clever and equally egotistical man from obtaining for himself a self-denying wife, for many women actually enjoy sacrificing themselves to their husbands. Men have different tastes and for them physical loveliness is usually of greater importance than any amount of intellectual ability and strength of character. Most men would regard marriage to a blue-stocking as being far too formidable an undertaking to embark on, so that intellectual cleverness may be a handicap to a woman in the marriage market. This is a pity, for the highly educated woman is usually too astute to parade her cleverness in front of her husband, and more often than not, makes an excellent wife and mother. The reason for this unpopularity of blue-stockings is probably that the educated woman is too new a phenomenon to be accepted yet as an ideal marriage partner.

But to attempt to make a catalogue of the female qualities which are attractive to men, and of the male qualities which are attractive to women, would be to attempt to explain what we agreed in Chapter One was impossible, that is, to explain the vagaries of sexual love. All that can be said on this subject with any profit has already been said, namely that men are more attracted by female loveliness and women more by a man's character and his attainments. Bulwer Lytton declared that no men were so courted by women in the earlier part of the nineteenth century as those who had achieved fame of one sort or another, even though the women in question were quite unable to understand what these men had actually done. According to him, the great scientist, Sir Humphry Davy, opened more love letters in a day than a gay guardsman opened in a year, and the octogenarian Wellington received many more adulatory epistles, as victor of Waterloo, than he had received in former years as the young and dashing but comparatively unknown, Colonel Wellesley.

As a result of the various sensory impressions reaching a man or woman from a member of the opposite sex, sexual desire is aroused, but it should not be concluded from this that the sexual urge is entirely dependent on sensory messages. Sexuality should be regarded rather as something which is innate in the individual, the proximity of an attractive member of the opposite sex being only the means by which this fundamental urge is aroused and made manifest. Another way of putting it would be to say that the female does not, by her mere presence, lead to the charging up of the male with sexual energy, but rather that she is the means by which his store of sexual energy is discharged. The same applies also to the action of the male on the female, that he provides facilities for the discharging of accumulated sexual energy. At the same time the proximity of an attractive member of the opposite sex does tend to strengthen sexuality in both parties.

All of the emotions give rise to physical changes in the body, which acts as a kind of sounding-board to the emotions. For example, fear is associated with pallor of the skin, dryness of the mouth, dilated pupils, cold sweats and a rapidly beating heart. The emotions of modesty and shame are manifested in the body by an aversion of the eyes and a reddening of the face. So also has sexual emotion its appropriate physical accompaniments, and by far the most striking of these is the physical phenomenon known as "tumescence". By this word is meant an engorgement with blood of certain sponge-like or erectile tissues in the body so that they become swollen and firmer. These sponge-like tissue are to be found in the combs and the wattles of the cock, in the breasts of mammals and they also enter largely into the construction of the genital organs, and particularly in the construction of the male external genital organ, the penis. In a state of sexual excitement these sponge-like tissues become "tumescent" or swollen, and after union has taken place they return to a state of "detumescence" or rest. These physical changes are associated with a disappearance of the former sexual tension and heightened desire. In Havelock Ellis's words: "Tumescence is the piling on of the fuel, detumescence is the leaping of the devouring flame whence is lighted the torch of life, to be handed on from generation to generation. In tumescence the organism is slowly wound up and force is accumulated; in the act of detumescence the accumulated force is let go, and by its liberation the sperm-bearing instrument is driven home."

In this chapter all that has been attempted has been to survey the part played by the special senses in the arousing of sexual desire. But attempts have been made by some people to go further than this, and to give an exact description of the ingredients of what is known as sex-appeal. Misguided efforts of this kind lead nowhere, for they leave out of account the many elements in sexual attraction which lie below the surface and admit of no measurement. The prize-winner of Hollywood's Sex Appeal Contest may possess all the measurements of the Venus of Milo, whilst another entrant may depart markedly from this Greek ideal of womanly beauty, yet it is the latter who will win the practical contests for sexual attractiveness outside of the studios of Hollywood. It is not correctness of measurements which counts in this greater world outside, for such trifles as the lift of an eyebrow, a sideward glance, a sudden change of facial expression, a huskiness in the voice, an unexpected gesture, are all capable of upsetting the calculations of the beauty statisticians.

In life it is quite possible to "fall in love" with such trifles as the lobe of an ear, a pouting lip, an eyebrow or a single wandering strand of hair. And it is equally possible to fall in love with the whole of the loved one and without in the least knowing why:

> "Yes, I'm in love, I feel it now
> And Celia has undone me;
> And yet I'll swear I can't tell how
> The pleasing plague stole on me.
> Tis not her face that love creates,
> For there no Graces revel;
> Tis not her shape, for there the Fates
> Have rather been uncivil.
> Tis not her air, for sure in that,
> There's nothing more than common;
> And all her sense is only chat,
> Like any other woman.
> Her voice, her touch, might give the alarm—
> Tis both perhaps or neither;
> In short 'tis that provoking charm
> of Celia altogether."
>
> (The *Je ne Sais Quoi* by William Whitehead.)

4

THE CHOOSING OF PARTNERS

IN the previous chapter courtship was described as the means by
which animals and men select their mates and an account was
then given of the process known as "falling in love". But
"falling" can scarcely be regarded as a reliable method of
choosing, for it is an accident and all choice has been eliminated
from the very start. "Falling in love" may have its own form
of logic but it is not the logic of reason and it was for this
reason that that astute old observer Dr. Samuel Johnson made
the remark that marriages in general would be as happy and
often more so, "if they were to be made by the Lord Chancellor
upon a due consideration of the character and circumstances,
without the parties having any choice in the matter".

And there are many people of a similar opinion to Dr. Samuel
Johnson for many things are required for the making of a
successful marriage in addition to sexual attraction. A large
measure of intellectual and emotional agreement in the couple
is desirable and this is not necessarily an ingredient of falling
in love, a process in which sexual attractiveness swamps all
other factors. Not that a clear line of demarcation can be drawn
between these various requirements, for in courtship intellectual
and emotional factors are closely interwoven with sexuality.
Even when a young man is discussing with a young woman
such seemingly neutral subjects as music, books, films and plays,
it is never very far away. This is quite natural and the only
reason for calling attention to it is in order to point out that

even when a relationship between a man and a woman appears to be based on common intellectual interests, sexual feeling may be playing a leading part. For as sexologists point out to us, sexuality has two sides to it, that of play and that of reproduction, and it was of the former that Havelock Ellis was speaking when he wrote: "Lovers in their play, when they have been liberated from the traditions which bind them to the trivial or the poor conception of play in love—are then moving amongst the highest human activities alike of the body and the soul. They are passing to each other the chalice of the wine which imparts the deepest joy that men and women know".

The much greater liberty accorded to young men and women of the present day allows of their getting to know each other much better before they become engaged than their parents and their grandparents were able to do. This is all to the good as is also the much greater freedom given to the girl in expressing her views and in either encouraging or discouraging the young man who is paying court to her. Our historical memories are remarkably short and it is difficult for us to realize today how strong was the emphasis placed by the Victorians on maidenly modesty and reserve. The following quotations on this subject are taken from Dr. Viola Klein's book "*The Feminine Character*".

"All the poets and prose-writers who have written upon love are agreed upon this point and that is that delicate reserve, a rosy diffidence and sweetly chastened deportment are precisely the qualities in a woman that mostly win upon the attention of men, whether young or old. The moment she begins to seek attention, she sinks in the esteem of any man with an opinion worth having."

"We cannot lend any countenance to such glaring impropriety as trying to 'catch the gentleman's attention'! It is *his* duty to try and catch yours; so preserve your dignity and the decorum due to your sex, position and usages in society."

"Mary F. is deeply in love with a young gentleman and wishes to know the best way to make him propose; she thinks he is fond of her, but is rather bashful. The best way is to wait. He will propose quite time enough. If Mary will give him a hint, he might run away."

"Lavina wants to get married—but cannot even obtain a sweetheart. She is afraid her commanding appearance intimidates the young gentlemen of her acquaintance. Nothing of the kind. It is her anxiety, her feverish stepping out of her maidenly reserve, which has shocked their preconceived notions of feminine propriety—and so frightened them into dumb significance. Lavina must be more retiring, think less of herself and learn to spell."

It was along these stern and uncompromising lines that the particular member of the staff of the *London Journal* who was responsible for the correspondence column dealt with the questions of the maidens of the Victorian Age. It would be interesting to know—but alas we shall never know—whether Lavina learnt to be more retiring, to think less of herself and to spell, and so in the end secured for herself a husband.

As has already been said, there are many motives for marrying in addition to the sexual motive and they are worthy of study if for no other reason than that many people remain entirely unaware of the real reason for their marrying. There is for example, that comparatively common case of the man who is not so much in love with a particular woman as with the idea of being in love. He has for long held enshrined in his heart the twin visions of the perfect wife and of the ideal marriage and having lit upon a girl who will serve as a lay figure for him, he projects on to her his dream. Having done this he is no longer capable of seeing her as she actually is, but only as he requires her to be. So also is there the woman who, ever since she was a girl, has been abstracting from story books and novels, her own conception of Prince Charming, and who invests the man who happens to be paying her some attention with all the required Prince Charming qualities. Both of these dreamers are experts in make-belief and it is astonishing what wonderful people they contrive to make out of very poor human material. Should they marry in this dream state there is bound to be a rude awakening for them. Although the story of Cinderella ends with the re-assuring words "They married and lived happily ever after-wards", it gives us no details of how Cinderella and her Prince managed to get along with each other after they had come up against the hard realities of life, say some five years later. It may be that they were still in love with each other but if so it was with a love of a richer, more understanding and enduring quality than the love with which they had started.

Other common reasons for two people marrying are loneli-ness, a desire for a home of their own, an ambition to partake of a fuller life than the one in which they have been brought up, a desire for children, or only for the purpose of escaping from the necessity of living any longer with their parents. All of these are possible and quite justifiable reasons for two people getting married, provided that there exists between them mutual affection, respect and a certain degree of sexual attraction.

Difficulties are more likely to arise in marriage when the two partners are of very different types and when they have had entirely different upbringings. It is sometimes said that opposites should marry and this statement contains an element of truth for, provided there be good will, opposite and complementary types have this great advantage that they are able to pool their assets and thus enjoy together a much richer life. But oppo-sites are not necessarily complementary to one another, and people who differ too fundamentally, or in too many respects, are likely to find the double harness of matrimony tiresome and even galling. For example, an active and extroverted husband who marries an introspective and idle wife may come to resent the fact that she thinks of nobody except herself and takes no interest at all in what *he* is doing. She on her part may be tempted to laugh at, or even to despise, the activities which he looks upon as being of such importance, and may come to treat her husband as an irresponsible child rather than as an adult man with whom it is possible to talk. So also is a marriage likely to show signs of strain when a business-like, methodical man marries an extremely artistic and temperamental wife, a woman who arrives at everything by "intuition" and who openly flouts his orderliness and his logic. It may of course happen that on many occasions she has arrived at precisely the same conclusions as he has arrived at, but the fact that they have travelled to them along different roads still makes it difficult for them to agree.

So also is it desirable that there should exist some small measure of agreement between a man and his wife concerning the great fundamental issues of life, and about such matters as religion. It is unnecessary for them to hold identical beliefs, but they must not stand so far apart that they are quite unable to understand each other's point of view. It is also helpful if there is some understanding about people, for if they dislike each other's friends their social life will be difficult. Again it is mutual understanding and not identity of taste which is needed.

Engaged couples are now able to discuss quite frankly whether or not they want children when they marry and this is to be welcomed, for it would be a mistake for a maternally minded girl to marry a man who would later refuse to allow her to have a child, or for a man who hoped to have a family to marry a wife with no desire for motherhood. But although the desirability or not of having a family is discussed by engaged couples there are very few young men and women who stop to think whether they have chosen wisely from the standpoint of future children. Not more than one man in ten wonders whether the girl by whom he is so strongly attracted has the makings in her of a good mother and even fewer girls ask themselves whether the men paying them attention are the kind of men they would select to be the fathers of their children.

Eugenics play a negligible part in the choice of marriage partners, and yet the health and the well-being of the future family are likely to be of immense importance to both of them in a comparatively few years time. As the result of this complete indifference on the part of people to the qualities which make for successful parenthood, many potentially ideal mothers remain unmarried, whilst women who are much less well fitted to bear children, but who happen to possess that indefinable quality known as sex appeal, quickly find husbands.

At an earlier period of history, all of these non-sexual and unromantic considerations were felt to be of such great importance that in many countries the choice of suitable marriage partners was entrusted to marriage specialists. The wise old men recognized as experts on this subject were aware of the fact that humanity is divisible into a comparatively small number of basic types, and a marriage will succeed only if the wedded pair belong to complementary or at any rate to compatible types. They not only knew this, theoretically, but were able to recognize the various types so that their help was always sought by those with marriageable sons and daughters. But this old science of human types has long been lost and the marriage experts of Persia, China and India have ceased to practice their art.

Questions are often asked about the importance of various disparities in the engaged couple, such things as a great discrepancy in age, differences of race and membership of different religions, and because dissimilarities of this kind are often important something must be said about them. The first problem, namely a marked difference in age, is the easiest to answer. If, as is more likely, it is the man who is the older of the two, the inequality is of far less importance than were it to be the other way round. Nevertheless, a girl who marries a middle-aged man will do well to bear in mind the fact that by the time she has become middle aged, her husband will be quite elderly and may no longer be able to satisfy her sexual needs. Not that this will be necessarily so, for there are men who have retained their potency into the eighties and so also are there women who have lost all sexual desire in the fifties. Moreover, if the other links between the two in the way of companionship and devotion to each other have become, by this time—as is quite likely to be the case—of far greater importance to them than sexual satisfaction, then the marriage will be able to withstand the strain caused by the snapping of some of its former links. But should comradeship, mutual respect and devotion be lacking in a marriage between people of markedly different age there is likelihood of trouble. The situation is less hopeful if it be the wife who is the older of the two, unless—and this is quite a common event—the man has sought in his marriage a mother surrogate rather than a wife. In marriages of this kind the sexual link between the two is generally a weak one and the disappearance of all sexual activity will scarcely be noticed. But to marry an older woman for protection and mothering is not a marriage in the fullest sense of that word and must be considered unnatural, as Orsino long ago pointed out to Viola in *Twelfth Night*.

> "... Let still the woman take
> An elder than herself; so wears she to him,
> So sways she level to her husband's heart;
> For, boy, however we do praise ourselves,
> Our fancies are more giddy and unfirm,
> More longing, wavering, sooner lost and won,
> Than women's are."

This same question of discrepancy of age may also have to be considered from the standpoint of future children and medical men are not infrequently asked whether the children are likely to suffer when one or both of their parents have passed their prime. Three statements can be made on this subject. The first is that on general principles the children of young parents are more likely to inherit robust health than are the children of middle aged and elderly parents. But age alone is seldom an absolute contra-indication to healthy, middle aged people having children. The second point is that the age of the mother is of far greater importance than the age of the father, and the third, that if the woman has borne a child earlier in her life then she is better able to continue child bearing into middle age without detriment, either to herself or to her children. It should of course be realized that whereas child-bearing is brought to an abrupt end in the woman by the onset of the menopause or change of life, procreation is still often possible to the male into a ripe old age. Instances of men in the eighties having children are quite common.

Another common question is whether cousins should be allowed to marry. In answering this question we have to accept the fact that human beings differ very little from cattle, so far as breeding is concerned. Since, therefore, intensive in-breeding has been practised with great success in the stockyards for many centuries, there is no intrinisc objection to cousins marrying. But for in-breeding to be desirable, the breeder must be certain that all objectionable *recessive* features have been eliminated from his herd, and the same principles must be applied to the marriage of cousins. When the family history with regard to inheritable trouble is excellent on both sides then there is no serious objection to their getting married. But unfortunately we can seldom be certain as the breeder is that all injurious recessive genes have been eliminated from human families. This being so marriages between cousins should be regarded as permissable when the health record on both sides is good, but on general principles they should not be encouraged.

It has already been pointed out, that few men and women consider the factor of health when selecting their life partners, and yet poor health is not only an obstacle to the rearing of a family but also to the happiness of the marriage itself. It is no easy lot to be married to a man in a precarious state of health, who is liable to lose his job at any moment and require nursing at home. So also is it difficult to be married to a continually ailing wife unable to look after the children or the home. Marriage complications of this kind have become still more formidable in these days when help in the home is well-nigh impossible to obtain and the cost of living is continually in the ascendant. Health therefore is a factor of considerable importance in the selection of a life partner.

Difference in social background, in religion and even in race have also to be considered. It is obvious that when two people have received similar educations, subscribe to the same religion, speak the same language and are members of the same race, much less adjustment will be required of them than when differences in these respects exist. It will be worth our while therefore to try to estimate their relative importance. Differences in social standing are becoming less and less difficult to deal with owing chiefly to a rise in the general level of education, for it is inequality of education in the two partners which is much more likely to give rise to marital difficulties than any inequalities of class. This was probably as true of such marriages in the past as it is true of them at the present day. The runaway match of the squire's daughter with one of her father's agricultural labourers was a highly successful affair so long as the romance lasted, but the real cause of the subsequent trouble and parting was not social inequality but the fact that the squire's daughter tired of being able to talk to her husband only about village gossip and local affairs. It was therefore the failure to find any interests in common outside those of the home which finally led to the wreckage of this romantic match.

Differences of race and language are also of importance, for marriages entail a bringing together, not only of a man and a woman, but also of their families and of their two circles of friends, and if none of these people can mix and learn to understand one another, disapproval and distrust will soon appear. The small discords which arise at the periphery of these two great circles will soon spread towards their centres, so that ultimately the husband and the wife will be implicated in the family quarrels. It must be remembered that all races and nations have their own way of managing their home affairs and their children. Small differences of opinion on such explosive subjects as the upbringing of children are liable to produce very big effects.

All of us attribute immense significance to the colour of a person's skin and when two people of markedly different complexions marry difficulties are multiplied a hundredfold. To a member of the so-called Aryan race (actually such things as pure races do not exist) the marriage of a white man to a negress and still more of a white girl to a negro, is utterly abhorrent and we have to accept the fact that this instinctive revulsion, on both sides, exists and that it is very deep-seated. No intellectual argument is capable of removing it for it is in the blood and beyond the range of reason. This does not necessarily mean that all mixed marriages of this kind are doomed to failure from the very start, but it certainly means that those who marry outside their racial colour are taking big risks. An additional objection which is often raised against such marriages is that the offspring resulting from them will inherit the bad qualities of both sides. Actually there exists no genetic justification for such a statement. It is quite true that half-breeds are usually ill-adjusted people, but this is not due to inherited deficiencies but to the great difficulties which half-breed children encounter from the very start and to the effect of this on their character. The short-comings of half-breeds are acquired and not inherited.

I have known hardheaded men, usually in the thirties or forties who have been so deeply aware of the risks attached to the accident of falling in love that they have gone to the oppo-site extreme and have dealt with the business of selecting a wife in the same cold and calculating spirit as that of a man choosing a reliable horse. I have even been consulted by such men con-cerning the advantages and disadvantages attached to wives of different size, build, and colour. Business-like men of this kind may find useful advice in wife-choosing in a book written long ago by Cobbett of *Rural Rides* fame. The following extracts have been taken from Cobbett's work *Advice to Young Men and (incidentally) to Young Women*.

"Look a little . . . in respect to a woman, at the labours of the teeth, for these correspond with those of the other members of the body, and with the operations of the mind. 'Quick at meals, quick at work', is a saying as old as the hills, in this, the most industrious nation upon earth; and never was there a truer saying. . . . Never mind the pieces of needlework, the tambouring, the maps of the world made by her needle. Get to see her at work upon a mutton-chop, or a bit of bread and cheese; and if she deal quickly with these, you have a pretty good security for that activity, that stirring industry, without which a wife is a burden instead of being a help. And, as to love, it cannot live for more than a month or two (in the breath of a man of spirit) towards a lazy woman.

" Another mark of industry is a quick step and a somewhat heavy tread, showing that the foot comes down with a hearty goodwill; and if the body lean a little forward, and the eyes keep steadily in the same direction, while the feet are going, so much the better, for these discover earnestness to arrive at the intended point. I do not like, and I never liked, young saunter-ing, soft-stepping girls, who move as if they were perfectly in-different as to the result, and as to the love part of the story, whoever expects ardent and lasting affection from one of these sauntering girls, will, when too late, find his mistake; the cha-racter runs the same all the way through; and no man ever yet saw a sauntering girl, who did not, when married, make a maw-kish wife, and a cold-hearted mother; cared very little for either by husband or children; and, of course, having no store of those blessings which are the natural resources to apply to in sickness and in old age . . ."

But unlike many men who are methodical and careful in selecting their mates, Cobbett was very quick off the mark when he did eventually meet a young woman who dealt quickly with chops and possessed the right action and body poise, for he wrote of the girl who became his wife: "When I first saw my wife she was thirteen years old and I was within about a month of twenty-one. She was the daughter of a sergeant of artillery and I was the sergeant major of a regiment of foot . . . I sat in the same room with her for about an hour in company with others and I made up my mind that she was the very girl for me. That I thought her beautiful is certain, for that I had always, said, should be an indispensable qualification; but I saw in her what I deemed marks of that sobriety of conduct about which I have said so much, which has been by far the greatest blessing of my life; from the day that I first spoke to her I never had a thought of her ever being the wife of any other man, more than I had thought of her being transformed into a chest of drawers!"

Quick though Cobbett was in assessing the qualities of the lady destined to be his wife, he was less rapid than Garibaldi.

In the biography of the great Italian patriot it is recorded that the boat in which he was travelling in South America was anchored one glorious evening about a hundred yards from the banks of an Uruguayan river. The future liberator of Italy was lying on the deck of it idly surveying the opposite shore, and more particularly a small Uruguayan hamlet, through a telescope. Suddenly the figure of a girl appeared in the field of view and Garibaldi fixed his gaze upon it. Two minutes later he put his telescope down, got into the dinghy tied on to the end of the yacht and rowed to the nearby shore. He had seen the girl he intended to marry. Not that he had ever met her before; she was a complete stranger to him, but unless he was very much mistaken she would marry him. She did, and his wife became one of his stoutest-hearted supporters, sharing with him all the dangers and hardships of his subsequent campaign in Italy. It proved to be an ideal marriage and, so far as I know, it is the only instance of a choice of partners made through a telescope.

5

PREPARATION FOR MARRIAGE

WHEN does preparation for marriage begin? It can be said to begin at birth, for all childhood experiences can be regarded as being a prelude to the experiences of adult life. Play is the child's dress rehearsal for the great events to come, and no game is played with more zest and thoroughness by the child than the game of family life. So also must the relationships between the boy and his mother and between the girl and her father be regarded as trial runs for the husband-wife relations to come. Dr. Ernest Jones, the biographer of Freud, lays stress on this and goes so far as to say that "success or failure in marriage is largely determined by the person's previous relationship to his parents."

It must be borne in mind that there is an unbroken continuity in the whole of our emotional life, and unresolved difficulties left over from the older child-parent relationship are often carried forward to be worked out later in the relationship between husband and wife. Nature is a careful account keeper, and the spoilt boy of yesterday becomes the equally spoilt husband of today. So also does the troublesome little girl become the troublesome little wife and for the very same reasons. Our characters change very little in the process of growing up, and underneath our newly acquired sophistication is to be found the former child, a little more complicated but otherwise the same. What we were yesterday has determined what we are today, and what we are today will decide what we are likely to be tomorrow.

A writer on the subject of marriage has suggested that before a youth proposes to a girl he should apply the three following tests to her; he should see her in a bathing dress, he should wake her up suddenly from sleep and note the first expression to come into her face, and he should visit her in her own home. Of the value of the first two tests I am unable to speak, but of the wisdom of the third recommendation I have no doubts. Not only will the said young man see what Ernest Jones deems to be of vital importance to success in marriage, the girl's relationship with her parents, but he will meet her mother, and what her mother is today she may be in some thirty years' time. We inherit more from our parents than we think.

But it is not with the choosing of partners that this chapter is concerned, but with preparations for marriage, and one important factor in the making of a successful marriage is the kind of introduction the girl or youth has had to the subject of sex. Many an adult's prospects of future happiness in marriage has been ruined long previously in the nursery and schoolroom. It is no exaggeration to say that half of the difficulties which crop up on the sexual side of marriage are the direct result of unskilful handling of one or other of the marriage partners during childhood. For example, many a man has been rendered impotent on his wedding night as the direct consequence of the pernicious nonsense written and spoken about the common practice of masturbation. So also is it likely that children who are reared in homes in which all manifestations of sexuality are looked upon as being either wrong or disgusting will continue to regard them as such, in the less conscious regions of their minds, long after they have grown up and married. The girl who has been terrified by tales about the horrors and perils of childbirth will remain terrified of them as a married woman. Nor is it always necessary for adults to express in words their own misconceptions on the subject of sex for harm of this kind to be done. Children are far more observant than we imagine and they are often able to sense their parents' feelings on the subject of sex, even though nothing has actually been said about it.

But such factors as the former child-parent relationship and the atmosphere of the homes in which the young man and the young woman were reared lie in the past and it is unlikely that there is anything to be done about them on the eve of the marriage. There are, however, many subjects of immediate concern to be discussed during the engagement and also practical things to be done during the last few months before the wedding. Amongst the most important of the decisions to be reached is the question of the future family. Are the engaged couple willing to have a child in the first year, if it should happen so, or would it be better to postpone this responsibility until they have adjusted themselves to each other and each other's ways? It is highly necessary, first, that an agreement should be reached on this subject, and second, that if their decision be to avoid an early conception, they should learn what is the right method of birth control to employ.

Had this book been written as little as sixty years ago, much space in this chapter would have been devoted to a discussion of the ethics of birth control. As short a time ago as 1932, whilst editing for the British Social Biology Council a work on marriage, I was compelled to write the following: "The fact that birth control has been a centre of bitter controversy and that a war of opinions is still raging around it, cannot be made an excuse for avoiding this thorny subject in a book which deals with marriage. Whatever we may feel, and however strong our reactions may be, it is impossible to deny that some method of controlling conception is being practised in the majority of homes." Fortunately, public opinion has changed since then, and it is no longer necessary for me to deal so tenderly with the topic of birth control. The Anglican Church has fully recognized the fact that there are occasions when it is inadvisable for a married couple to bring children into the world, and it has agreed that in such circumstances birth control is justifiable. For example, no humane person could countenance the bringing into the world of children who ran a grave risk of inheriting some grave congenital deformity or family disease. Nor could anyone desire that births should follow in such rapid succession that the health of the mother should suffer.

The question which is being discussed in this chapter is not whether the couple in question should or should not have a family, but whether they should have it now or a little later on. Many arguments could be put forward in favour of postponing the arrival of the first child for a year or two. In these days of high taxation and of the scarcity of domestic help, it may be very difficult for a young couple of very limited means to undertake at once the additional cost of children. There is also much to be said in favour of their adjusting themselves to each other before assuming the additional responsibilities of parenthood. Adler once described marriage as a constructive task of two persons of opposite sex who are determined to live together in order to relieve and enrich each other's lives, and it is almost unnecessary to add that this is a task which requires a great deal of patient and devoted work by both parties. A good case may therefore be made for postponing the responsibilities of parenthood for a year or two, provided that both husband and wife are still young. Equally cogent arguments can also be brought in favour of the contrary decision *not* to postpone the arrival of a family, and the most important of these is that the use of birth control measures complicates the sexual act considerably and that newly-wed people have enough to learn without making things more difficult for themselves by having to use birth-control devices.

Should the decision be reached that for one reason or another it is better for the couple to postpone having children, the next step will be to find out how this can best be achieved. Either the right kind of doctor will have to be consulted, or else the future bride will have to visit one of the special clinics established for the express purpose of giving advice on birth control, such as a Family Planning Association Clinic. The first doctor most likely to be approached on this will be the family doctor, who will either deal with the matter himself or else will refer the future bride to the right expert. Whatever be done, the obtaining of advice should not be delayed for too long, for it is quite possible that a certain amount of preliminary dilatation will have to be carried out before the occlusive pessary usually prescribed can be fitted. Should this dilatation be necessary, it will have to be completed at least a month before the wedding. The subject of contraception will be discussed in greater detail in Chapter 12.

There are other matters which may have to be settled before the wedding. For example, there are writers on this subject who urge that both partners should submit themselves to a routine medical overhaul, whether special advice on the subject of birth control be needed or not. There are indeed, doctors who go so far as to say that a pre-marital examination of this kind is of such supreme importance that it ought to be made compulsory, as it has already been made compulsory in Sweden. Personally I should deplore adding yet another official compulsion to the many we have to put up with, but I do not deny that there is much to be said in favour of a voluntary medical overhaul of the two people concerned. Several advantages might accrue from an examination of this kind; it would reduce the risk of anyone marrying unwittingly in a highly precarious state of health, and it would also bring to light physical defects which might later prove to be an obstacle to the consummation of the marriage. For example, a narrow female passage protected by a particularly tough hymen might be found, which, discovered in good time, could easily be dealt with, thus avoiding much future frustration during the honeymoon. So also would any risk of either party marrying with latent venereal disease be avoided by a pre-marital examination. There are cases also in which an examination of the man's semen is indicated, in order to make sure that his fertility has not been damaged by some previous illness, for a girl has the right to know whether or not she has a reasonable chance of becoming a mother. All of these advantages can be gained from a pre-marital medical examination, but personally I think that it is unnecessary to make such an examination obligatory.

Wars are almost always followed by a steep rise in the incidence of venereal disease, and a strong case was made in favour of a pre-marriage medical examination a few years ago on the grounds that it would be a safeguard against the possible transmission from one party to the other of unsuspected venereal disease. This argument still holds good although venereal disease is no longer the scourge it formerly was, thanks to the discovery of penicillin and the various M and B drugs. As many people have a horror of venereal diseases and as much ignorance still exists on this subject, something will have to be said about it.

There are two common venereal diseases, gonorrhœa and syphilis and both are transmitted by sexual contact. It is of course possible to contract them in other ways, such as through the use of an infected towel or lavatory seat, but this indirect manner of transmission is comparatively rare. Gonorrhœa is ten times commoner than syphilis and is the result of the infection of the urethra with a micro-organism known as the gonococcus. Some forty-eight hours after infection has occurred a urethral discharge appears together with smarting on passing urine. It is important to realize that all urethral discharges are not gonoccal. It is equally necessary to know that the germs of gonorrhœa may persist in the urethra long after obvious discharge has disappeared and other signs of inflammation have subsided. If therefore either of the engaged couple is aware of the fact that he or she has suffered from gonorrhœa in the past it is essential that a careful bacteriological investigation should be made in order to ensure that no infection remains.

The symptoms and signs of gonorrhœa in the female are a copious vaginal discharge and smarting and frequency in passing urine. Again it must be said that all vaginal and urethral discharges in women are not gonococcal discharges and that a careful bacteriological examination has to be made to establish a diagnosis. This can only be done by an expert bacteriologist.

So also is it advisable that any person who has suffered from syphilis in the past and who now intends to marry should consult a doctor before doing so.

Fortunately, the outlook with regard to both these diseases has been entirely altered during the last twenty years, and no one need be terrified by the thought of them any longer. It is necessary to make this statement because many people still regard the two with the utmost horror. So much may anxiety prey on their minds on this subject that they may easily become the victims of a neurosis. Venereophobia, or fear of being infected with venereal disease, is a very definite clinical entity and I have known patients go from doctor to doctor and from clinic to clinic under the delusion that they are suffering from undiagnosed venereal disease. It matters not how often they are tested or how frequently they are reassured, they still remain convinced that they have contracted venereal disease.

Blood tests for syphilis are well known to the public but there is a great deal of confused thought on the subject. The Wasserman reaction, as it is called, is of the greatest value in arriving at a diagnosis but it is of no use in the earliest stage of the disease. The primary lesion of syphilis—the chancre—is diagnosed, not from the reaction of the patient's blood, but from the discovery of the *spirochaeta pallida* in its secretions. And even in the later stages of the disease the blood reaction is an aid to diagnosis rather than the hub round which everything turns. This does not mean that it is not a very valuable test; it only means that the Wasserman report should always be viewed against the background of other medical findings.

Finally it is necessary that before marrying both partners should possess at least an elementary knowledge of the sexual act. Some readers may think that a statement of this kind is superfluous since it is highly unlikely that anybody would be so foolish as to marry without any knowledge of the act of love-making. I can assure such readers that a warning of this nature is urgently needed. I have in my files records of many people who married in a state of abysmal ignorance, and one striking instance of this can be given. It was the case of a solicitor of forty years of age who came to me two years after his wedding because it had at last dawned on him that something was missing in his married life. It was; he proved to be far more ignorant of what are known as the "facts of life" than are the great majority of schoolboys. And he is not the only case in my files of a man marrying in a state bordering on complete innocence.

The reason why people marry so unprepared for what is to happen after the wedding is that they fondly believe that everything "will come naturally when the time arrives for it. Why therefore should they bother to seek advice from medical men or read books on such an indelicate subject?" But in the case of the civilized man, instinct has almost always to be supplemented with learning, for instinct in the town dweller is far less alert and less reliable than in the man living close to Nature. We do not trust a woman's maternal instinct to supply her with all the information necessary for the proper care of the baby, but either send her to a child welfare clinic, or else give her a book to read on mothercraft. So also is it necessary for both partners, and particularly for the male partner, to acquire some knowledge of the art of love-making before the wedding night.

Women are often as ignorant of this subject as are the men and they are even more disposed than men to believe that everything will come quite naturally when the proper time arrives for it. And with good fortune everything may happen as these optimistic women hope but only if they are marrying men who have previously had experience of sexual intercourse. But as likely as not they are marrying men who are as ignorant of the arts of love-making as themselves. Gynaecologists tell us that it is no rarity to find in their clinics patients who have been married for several years without their husbands ever having penetrated them. It is true that some sort of intercourse has taken place between themselves and their husbands, but not of a nature that would be likely to result in what they have been longing for all this time, that they should produce a child.

It is strange that such gross ignorance should still survive amongst the highly educated people of today, for some of the men and women of whom I am speaking have been unusually well educated. Fortunately, steps are now being taken to give children a much better biological, and even a better sexual education, than they formerly received and this, together with the publication of many satisfactory books on this subject, is likely to lead eventually to a reduction of the number of adults who marry in a state of sexual ignorance.

But all books suffer from the defect that they cannot be questioned, and many of those who are about to marry have personal problems of a sexual nature on which they would like to have advice. For such people as these a human counsellor is much to be preferred, and the question arises as to whom they should go for such advice. A few writers on this subject have suggested that they should obtain advice from the man whom they are bound to visit in any case before the wedding day, namely, the clergyman who is going to marry them. Now I quite agree that there are excellent clerical marriage counsellors who have specially equipped themselves for this expert work, but they are very few in number, and there are undoubtedly grave disadvantages in consulting a clergyman. The first of these is that the clergy as a class are particularly ignorant about the subject of sex, and the second that they are far more interested in the moral issues of sexuality than in any of its physical and psychological problems. For example, I have never yet met a clergyman who recognized that masturbation, at a certain stage of sexual development, could be looked upon as being a physiological rather than an immoral act.

In my opinion the family doctor is a much better choice, but some family doctors, although excellent in every other way, show very little interest in sex problems and have had no experience of how to deal with them. Having satisfied themselves that there is nothing physically wrong with the candidates for marriage, they are likely to assure them that there is no need for them to worry, and then with wishes for a long and happy married life the interview is brought to an end. Little will be gained from a pre-marital consultation of this truncated kind, for should sexual difficulties be encountered after the wedding, they will be of a psychological rather than a physical nature, and as such they can only be discovered after a long and intimate talk between the doctor and the candidate for marriage.

The family doctor who has had more experience of such psychological difficulties is well aware of this fact, and should the girl seem fearful of what is going to happen to her, or should the man appear to be convinced that he will fail as a husband—it is much more likely to be the male partner who is worried—he will either deal with the inhibiting fear himself or else will refer his patient to the right expert. I have in my files many records of patients with serious sexual neuroses who had previously been assured by their doctors that all would be well on their wedding night when actually they were badly in need of psychiatric treatment before they married. The family doctor's reassurance is an excellent remedy for lesser degrees of anxiety, provided that there exists no serious sexual deviation or inhibition which requires more expert psychological handling. When therefore any doubt exists in the practitioner's mind he would be well advised to pass on the responsibility of deciding whether marriage is advisable or not, to a psychiatrist.

The liberty allowed to the young of both sexes at the present time has the great advantage that it allows them to get to know each other much better than their grandparents knew each other before their wedding. But it is not without disadvantages. As has already been said, sexuality is never far away from an engaged couple, and it is difficult for any line to be drawn between what society accepts as permissible and what it regards as unpermissible. Many engaged couples abandon earlier attempts to draw any line at all between the two with the result that friendship passes gradually into courtship, and courtship passes equally smoothly into a kind of trial marriage. Now whatever our views as older and more responsible people may be, it would be a mistake to lay too much blame for this on the younger generation, for the transition takes place so naturally and so inevitably that it is scarcely noticed. So also have we to bear in mind a fact which has already been stressed, that courtship is not only the process of selecting partners, but also the means by which the latent sexuality of the engaged couple is set in motion. Finally, we have to realize that Nature has made no provision for engagements but only for marriages.

It is not the purpose of this book to drive home any particular brand of sexual ethics, and it will be left to the reader to reach his or her conclusions on this difficult problem of the anticipation of marriage by engaged couples. That engaged couples do in fact frequently forestall marriage is shown by the Kinsey Reports, which state that fifty per cent. of the women interviewed admitted pre-marital sex relations, many of them with the men whom they subsequently married. Preparation for marriage is being considered here chiefly from the physiological and anthropological angles, and the briefest excursion into anthropology shows that the rules regulating pre-marital behaviour differ very widely in different parts of the world. Some races demand that the bride shall be a virgin, others, whilst not insisting on virginity, set a premium on it, and yet others allow the young unmarried of both sexes great pre-nuptial freedom. There is, never has been, and is never likely to be, any unanimity on this subject.

Malinowski studied the marriage and pre-marriage customs of the South Sea islanders, and he made the startling discovery that the Trobriand islanders knew so little about the part played by the male in reproduction, that a Trobriand islander on returning home after a year's absence, would often be delighted to learn that his wife was expecting a child. For people as simple as this, sexual ethics have become a very simple matter. Malinowski reports that on other islands it was the custom for young unmarried people of both sexes to share mats in the communal sleeping huts. Changes of partners occasionally took place in these huts, but promiscuity was frowned upon, and changes were consequently much less common than might have been supposed. When a young man and woman found that they were suitably mated and that they had grown so fond of each other that they disliked being apart, arrangements were made for their marriage. Presents were exchanged, the wedding was celebrated, and the couple retired into their own hut. The method by which conception was avoided previously before their marriage was unascertainable, but should a young woman conceive, a marriage was immediately arranged, since the lack of a father handicapped the child.

In the simple communities of the Pacific Islands, this method of choosing mates appeared to work admirably, but this does not necessarily mean that it would be equally successful under the much more complicated conditions of Western life. Judge Lindsay of the U.S.A., advocated what he called "trial or novitiate marriages" some thirty years ago, but he never received for this idea anything more than theoretical support and I think it would be true to say that the great majority of writers on this subject were bitterly opposed to it. Some of them expressed the opinion that flouting, as it does, the prevalent Western code, a trial marriage of this kind cannot be regarded as being in any way a satisfactory rehearsal for married life. Moreover, some of those who have had recourse to trial marriage neither took the trial run seriously nor endeavoured to make it work, and this meant that the so-called rehearsal for real marriage was abused. Such was the consensus of opinion on the subject of Judge Lindsay's idea of trial marriage. But this does not mean that all trial marriages of this kind are to be deplored, for a large percentage of them have led to a permanent and highly successful union. All that I personally am able to say with assurance on this highly controversial subject is that although I have seen many failures of trial or novitiate marriages, I have also seen many striking successes. The most weighty objection that can be brought against them is the theoretical one that they may weaken the institution of marriage, and since we have accepted marriage as a necessity to our culture, anything which weakens it is unwelcome.

Whatever our views may be on the subject of trial marriages, long engagements are to be deplored on account of the strain they impose on both the man and the woman. This strain can manifest itself physically in the man as a chronic and painful congestion of the testicles. In the girl it is more likely to show itself in emotional disturbances which are sometimes of sufficient intensity to lead to a breaking off of the engagement.

Society has drawn an arbitrary line between what is permissible and what is not permissible to engaged people, and as we have already seen, this line is an entirely fictitious one. As a result of society's rule, there is need for a continual drawing back on the part of the engaged persons, an access of affection being immediately followed by its suppression, and it is not in the least surprising that in the case of many couples, the conventional line is frequently overstepped so that the practice known in America as "necking" and "petting" is begun. Such intimacies as these have a proper place in the love-play which is a prelude to the sexual act, but employed alone they may cause mischief. Not only can they become a substitute for complete union, even after the two are married, but they tend to leave the genital organs of both parties in a state of chronic congestion. If an engaged couple has trespassed into forbidden territory as far as this, then surely it would be better for them to go the whole way. Reputations for chastity have already been lost and nothing has been gained in exchange. Such practices as "necking" and "petting" are very unsatisfactory methods of dealing with the troubles of a long engagement and they should be discouraged.

6

SEXUAL CHARACTERISTICS OF
MEN AND WOMEN

In Chapter Four some of the psychological characteristics of the two sexes were discussed and in this chapter attention will be directed to differences in the sexual responses of men and women. This is a necessary preliminary to the study of sexual intercourse which is the subject matter of the two following chapters. In order to understand differences in the attitudes of men and women to sexuality it will be necessary to start at the very beginning with the development of the sexual characteristics of the two sexes.

It is now established that the sex of the new individual is decided at the moment of conception, and that any effort on our part to produce a male or a female by subsequent treatment, dietetic or otherwise, of the pregnant mother is quite useless. Nothing we can do will alter what was long ago decided when the spermatozoon met and fertilized the ovum. In mammals two types of spermatozoa are produced which have been called by the biologists, X-bearing and Y-bearing spermatozoa. The female produces only one type of ovum the X-bearing ovum, and this uniform egg cell can be fertilized by either variety of spermatozoon, by an X-bearing spermatozoon so as to produce XX, a female, or by a Y-bearing spermatozoon so as to produce XY, a male.

The above is true of mammals, but in birds, moths and butterflies it is the other way round and the ovum which determines the sex of the offspring. In these creatures there exists a single type of spermatozoon but two varieties of ova, so that it is the mother in these orders which decides the sex of the off-spring.

Although the sex of the human embryo is decided from the very start, a long time will have to pass before we are able to determine by our examination of it to which sex the embryo belongs. In the human embryo this decision is not likely to be made until between the fifth and seventh week of gestation, by which time the embryonic cells forming the sex glands will be sufficiently differentiated to allow us to decide whether the glands are going to develop into testicles or ovaries. What makes the settling of the embryo's sex much more difficult is that it has a foot in both camps, possessing the rudimentary duct systems and the external organs of both sexes. In other words, we all start our lives as hermaphrodites, capable of moving in the direction of the male or the female. If we move in the male direction, the male side of our dual equipment will be developed at the expense of the female side of it, and if we are to become females, the female side will develop at the expense of the male. But whichever of these events happens to us we shall retain for the rest of our lives certain rudimentary vestiges of the opposite sex.

Experiments have shown that the factor which decides whether the bisexual genital system shall turn in the male or in the female direction is the secretion of the primary genital glands, that is to say, the testicles and the ovaries. If these primary sexual glands are testicles, their internal secretions will impel the body in a male direction; if they are ovaries they will push it in a female direction. But there is a slight difference in the mechanism of development in different animals, for it would appear that the human body and the body of the mammal have a distinct bias in the direction of femaleless, so that a stronger push has to be imparted to it by the testicles to make a satisfactory male of it than the push required to produce a satisfactory female out of it. The converse of this is true of birds. Here the bias of the body is towards maleness, as is shown by the fact that if the ovaries of a pullet are destroyed by disease, it is liable to turn into a cockerel.

Many experiments have been carried out in laboratories to demonstrate the foregoing facts, and various forms of *inter-sex* have been produced by castrating young animals and grafting on to them the glands of the opposite sex. All these experiments, as well as those which spontaneously occur in Nature, show that the machinery which controls the development of sex characteristics is rather complicated. In his *Science of Life*, H. G. Wells refers to this machinery as a piece of dual switch mechanism. The chromosomes of the parents' "sex cells (the spermatozoa and the ova) work the first switch; set in a certain way the animal begins to travel a certain road, so as to produce male sex glands, but set in another way it travels along another road and produces ovaries. At this point in the animal's development, there is situated the second switch which acts by turning on supplies of either male or female hormones. It is with this switch that we have learned to tamper so as to divert the development of the animal in the opposite direction and produce various degrees of feminized males and of masculinized females. And it is also by the occurrence of some mishap at this switch that the various degrees of inter-sex produced by Nature are likely to be explained."

As a result of this brief biological survey of the development of the sexual characteristics, we can see that the popular view of the two sexes is in need of correction. Masculine and feminine are not, as so many people suppose, two well defined and separate entities standing wide apart on their separate sites. We must regard them as two conditions which may approach each other and "end by fusing in a state of primitive ambiguity" (Marañon). In every male there lurks a female, in every female a male, so that we have to look upon sexuality as a long keyboard in which every kind of note is being sounded, from the deep base of the most masculine male to the highest treble of the most feminine female.

This new attitude to sex will help us to understand better not only such rarities as true hermaphroditism and spontaneous changes of sex in animals, but also certain psychological deviations of sexuality. It should also make us more liberally minded towards our fellow men, for, as Biedl has put it, "the pure man and the pure woman" are extreme cases which are scarcely ever to be met with. In former times, before these facts were known, for anyone to cast doubt on the masculinity of a man or on the femininity of a woman was the worst insult which could possibly be offered them. So also all inter-sexual states, whether they manifested themselves on the physical or the psychological plane, were looked upon with intense horror. But this was an entirely false and unscientific way of looking upon sex. We are all strange mixtures of masculinity and femininity, and the unhappy inter-sexual individuals from whom people turned away with such aversion in former days are merely the middle notes of the long keyboard stretching between the two extremes of the intensely masculine male and the equally feminine female. This subject will be dealt with in greater detail in Chapter 21.

Having cleared away certain obstacles to understanding, we are now in a position to discuss differences in the two sexes in the functioning of their sexuality and also the different attitudes of men and women to the sexual act. In the first place, it can be said that desire in men is more generally uniform than it is in women. Another way of putting this would be to say that women are the extremists and men are the moderates with regard both to sex and to the emotions. This truth is reflected in such old sayings as; "the best angels in heaven and the worst devils in hell are all feminine". Whilst marked variations are found in the intensity of the sexual drive amongst men, the differences are much less marked amongst men than amongst women. In other words, many more cases of excessive passion or nymphomania and of complete indifference to sexuality, or frigidity, are to be found amongst women than amongst men.

A second difference is that desire in men is less dependent on the presence of a desirable love object than is desire in women. By this is meant that in men sexuality has more the character of a physiological drive which has its origin in a rhythmic stimulation of the sex organs so that it is able to manifest itself in the complete absence of any external exciting case. In a woman sexuality works less independently than it does in the case of a man. A woman develops sexual desire not because of some impersonal sex urge but because a strong emotion has been evoked in her by the presence of some particular man. She has a desire for him because she is in love with him and wishes to express her love for him in this way. Sexuality for sexuality's sake alone has much less attraction for her than it has for a man. She requires not only that the man with whom she is in love should be her partner in this love-making, but that the setting for their love affair should also be right, and she is often very exacting about the rightness of this setting. When a woman gives herself to a man everything must be in harmony with what she is doing; the hour, the place, everything has to be in keeping with the occasion, and the understanding between herself and her lover must also be complete. There must be no jarring note, and foremost of all her requirements is that the love intercourse between them must be something more than a physical act. "The way to my senses is through my heart", wrote Mary Wollstonecraft to her lover Finlay, "but forgive me! I think there is sometimes a shorter cut to yours". She was right. In the male there is a more abrupt and quicker way to the sexual act than through the intermediary of the heart, namely, the short cut provided by crude sensuality. Unlike a woman, a man is often content with purely physical form of satisfaction, with an act unaccompanied by any stirring of the emotions on either side. In other words, he can put up quite easily with sex for sex's sake. Sexual intercourse for many men is little more than a sensuous physiological function.

Women have always been aware of this important difference between their love and that of a man and they have frequently called attention to it. Ellen Kay writes of the different attitudes of the two sexes to love in *Love and Marriage* as follows: "It is without doubt a feminine exaggeration to say that a 'pure' woman only feels the force of her sex's need when she loves. But the enormous difference between her and a man is at present this: that he more often gives of his best as a creator than as a lover—while for her the reverse is nearly always the case. And while thus appraised by himself and others according to his work, woman in her heart values herself—and wishes to be valued—according to love. Not until this is fully appreciated and working for happiness does she feel her worth. It is no doubt true that a woman also wishes to be made happy by a man through her senses. But while this longing in her not infrequently awakes long after she already loves a man so that she could give her life for him, with man the desire to possess a woman often wakes before he even loves her enough to give his little finger for her."

Because of this difference in the attitudes of the two sexes to sexuality it has been said that man is by nature polygamous and woman monogamous. I am very doubtful of the truth of this, and attribute a woman's greater fidelity in marriage, to the fact that sexual intercourse has much weightier consequences for her than for a man. It is natural, therefore, that she should be more careful about giving herself to a lover, but if she is really in love with a man other than her husband, then she is capable of showing remarkable courage in flouting the opinion of her friends and following her heart's lead.

Because sexuality in a man is less dependent on other conditions than is sexuality in a woman, because it is, so to speak, in a man's blood, ready to leap up at any moment, a few words or a simple gesture is quite sufficient to excite him. But for sexuality to be aroused in a woman, far more than this is usually required, and this is, of course, particularly true of women without any previous sexual experience. In inexperienced women sexuality lies ready to be awakened but it is frequently still asleep in them and this is perhaps the most important of all the differences between the two sexes when they are looked at from the viewpoint of this chapter. It is a difference of which every husband should take note, that although he is in full possession of his sexual desire and of his sexual powers—though not yet of the refinements of love-making—his wife is probably in an entirely different position. In her, sexual desire lies dormant, waiting to be aroused by him, a state of affairs which throws a very heavy responsibility on him. If he is abrupt and clumsy, if he allows his own fierce desires to master him then he may destroy, and perhaps for good, the whole of his wife's sexual future. It is no light task, this, that he will have to discharge after his marriage, this task of awakening sexual desire in his wife and teaching her the arts of love-making. As Mary Wollstonecraft rightly observed a woman's sexual feelings have to be approached by way of her heart and not through the abrupt gateway of the senses. And much will depend on the way the husband discharges his responsibilities. If he initiates his wife skilfully into the mysteries of sexuality, they will add richness to her emotional life, but if he is thoughtless or brutal in his approach to her she is likely to acquire an entirely negative attitude to sexuality and all its manifestations. "Do not begin your marriage with a rape", wrote Balzac, and that great French novelist and humanitarian knew a great deal about sexuality and women.

Many women look back upon their wedding night as the greatest occasion in the whole of their lives. This being so, and wedding nights and honeymoons being what they usually are, compounded of ecstacy and disillusionment, delight and disappointment, extravagant joys and momentary sorrows, many women recall their wedding nights and their honeymoons with strange and often with contradictory feelings. For few honeymoons ever attain that exalted level of bliss which was expected of them. They are usually lit by moments of supreme happiness, but it is too much to expect of any human relationship and particularly of the relationship of two people on their honeymoon that there should not also be fleeting disappointments and griefs. No, mistakes have almost always to be made during this period of apprenticeship to love and marriage, for love making and living happily together are arts, and arts cannot be mastered in a few days. Complete harmony can only be reached after much practice and with the exercise of much patience. This being so, the first lesson to be learnt about honeymoons is that they are apprenticeships to love rather than festivals of achievement. But this very fact that the two lovers are apprentices who are learning their new calling together, two people who are sharing each other's triumphs and mistakes, will act as another bond between them.

It has already been stressed that sexuality is far more closely linked in a woman with her emotions than in a man, and it is also true that it is much more closely associated in her mind with the idea of parenthood than is the sexuality of a man. As Marañon has put it, a woman "experiences an inclination towards a sexual life only in order to utilize the man as a detour towards a maternal end". The urge to possess a child is so fundamental in her that it colours all her sex life. This is one of the several reasons why Judge Lindsay's novitiate or trial marriage can never be regarded as a genuine dress-rehearsal for a real marriage, since in a trial marriage contraceptive measures must always be used.

Two other differences between the sexualities of a woman and a man remain to be discussed. The first is that sexual feeling in a woman is not strictly localized, as it is in a man, in the genital organs but is diffused widely throughout the whole of her body. There are, also, certain erogeinous areas in the woman's body, such as the breasts and lips, areas which contain a variable amount of erectile tissue and which, when stimulated, are specially likely to arouse desire. Because of the extensiveness of the area over which sexuality is spread, a woman is capable of experiencing an orgasm or sexual climax by the stimulation of the extra-genital regions of her body alone without penetration of the genital passages having occurred. The importance of this fact to her husband and the use to which he can put his knowledge of it will be discussed in the next two chapters.

The final difference between the sexual reactions of the two sexes to be discussed concerns the sexual climax or orgasm. The orgasm of the man is entirely bound up with the act of ejaculation or the throwing out of the semen, an event which may occur within a few minutes of the beginning of active intercourse. The orgasm in a woman, like her sexual desires, seems to be much less closely linked with her sexual organs than are the corresponding events in a man, although certain rhythmic movements of a rather indefinite nature often occur in the woman's uterus or womb at the moment of her orgasm. Another characteristic of the woman's orgasm is that it is more capricious than is the organism of a man. So belated is its appearance in many women that it may have happened only a few times in their lives and then merely, because for one reason or another, coitus has lasted for an unusually long time. Many women therefore have come to look upon an orgasm as a luxury of which they are usually deprived owing to the fact that their husbands reach their climax long before they have had time to attain it. And from one standpoint, namely, that of functional efficiency, they are right in affirming that Nature has been unfair to them in this matter for whereas for the right working of the reproductive organs of a man an ejaculation is indispensable, for the right functioning of the reproductive organs of a woman a climax or orgasm is quite unnecessary and consequently a luxury. There are many mothers of large families who have never experienced an orgasm in the whole of their lives. But this subject of the capriciousness of the orgasm in a woman will be discussed much more fully in the following two chapters.

7

THE CONSUMMATION OF MARRIAGE

ACCORDING to tradition, the consummation of a marriage should take place on the first night of the honeymoon but this is a rule as much honoured in the breach of it as in any blind following of it. Love should be bound by no rules. As often as not both bride and bridegroom are tired on their wedding night and the former is particularly likely to be exhausted by all the excitements, emotions and events of the day. The wedding ceremony, the subsequent reception, the bidding goodbye to relations and friends, the journey by railway or car to an hotel, all of these events, coming perhaps on the top of several weeks of preparing for the wedding, have tired her out and she may well be more inclined for sleep than for embarking on something which, for her, may seem a very formidable undertaking. If this be so then it is much better that little more should take place on this their first night together, beyond the endearments and caresses which they have been accustomed to exchange during their engagement. It is for the husband to judge what is best for his wife on her bridal night and to consider her feelings and her physical state rather than any convention about wedding nights and, if he has judged rightly in giving precedence to his wife's feelings rather than to his own desires then she will always recall how he treated her on her wedding night with gratitude.

Another statement that can be made on this subject of honeymoons is that it is highly unlikely that the first essays in love-making by a newly-wed husband and wife, unversed in the art of love will be completely satisfactory. At the beginning mistakes are bound to be made, things left undone which should have been done, and things done which ought not to have been done. It is by trial and error that most new things are learnt and this being so a newly-wed couple cannot expect sexual harmony to be attained at the very start. What makes this still less likely is that no person ever approaches his or her first trial of love-making with an entirely open mind, but with a mind which has been conditioned by all that has happened in the past, and in a past which stretches right back to the earliest days of childhood. And who knows what may not have happened during that time? Because of a faulty sexual upbringing, because of some fear implanted into her the bride may be awaiting the first intimacies of married life with terror, forcing her body to yield to her husband's advances but dreading it all the time. She may be able to give her body to her husband but she will be quite incapable of yielding also herself and her feelings. Nor is it necessarily only the bride who is apprehensive about the first intercourse. If her husband is without any previous experience of love-making and has doubts about his own sexual capacity—as many men have —he may also be in a nervous state. Patience and forbearance are required on both sides during the earlier days of the honeymoon.

Sexual intercourse is usually divided for convenience of description into the three phases; first, love-play and courtship, second, sexual union and third, the epilogue, or what Van de Velde prefers to call the after-glow. Each stage passes imperceptibly into that which follows it so that no sharply dividing line can or should be drawn between the one and the other. It can be said of sexual intercourse that it recapitulates in miniature the previous emotional history of the two lovers, but that it now expresses this history in a fullness of which it was previously deprived. The first phase represents the earlier period of their courtship but accompanied now with the caresses and endearments from which the husband was formerly compelled to refrain. By words and actions he expresses his love and his desire for his wife, fondling her, not only with his lips and his hands, but with the whole of his body. As has previously been said, touch leads most quickly to the arousing of sexual feeling and there are certain erogenous zones in the body which when fondled have a particularly strong exciting effect on sexual desire. These desire-producing areas are usually situated where skin joins up with mucous membrane places, regions such as the lips and the breasts. Fondling of the breasts takes an important place in love-play and it may be said that one of the differences between the expert and the beginner in love-making is that the former makes much greater use than the latter of his hands during the whole of the sexual act, and particularly during this first stage of love-play. At this time the husband's hands are as active as are his lips, travelling over the whole of the loved one's body, pausing for a moment and then passing on to caress some new region. The approach to the most intimate region of all, the external female genitalia and more especially to the highly important female organ, the clitoris, is always an indirect one. It is a drawing nearer to it at one moment and then a retreating elsewhere until the lover is encouraged by signs of consent on the part of the loved one and is able to enjoy the still greater intimacies he seeks.

So also do kisses play a large part in love-play, which amongst Western races almost always starts with a kiss. There are of course conventional types of kiss which having nothing at all to do with love. There are also kisses of a slightly more sexual nature which are given and received so hastily that they are unlikely to lead on to anything else. Both of these varieties of kiss lack the special character of the erotic kiss. The erotic kiss is a lingering kiss given and received from mouth to mouth with mutual pressure.

There are a great many forms of erotic kiss. To quote Dr. Van de Velde: "It (the erotic kiss) may 'brush the bloom' like a butterfly's wing by a light stroking of lips with other pursed lips; be, as it were, an 'effleurage,'" to use the technical term of massage therapy for gentle stroking, and of poetry for fleeting, hardly perceptible contacts. From its lightest, faintest form, it may run the gamut of intimacy and intensity to the pitch of *Maraichinage*, in which the couple, sometimes for hours, mutually explore and caress the inside of each other's mouths with their tongues, as profoundly as possible. But it is indisputable that the greatest penetration in kissing is not for *all* lovers the same as the maximum pleasure and stimulation. Mastership of this art is a matter of delicate differences rather than of *one* limited and sharply defined style.

"But the *tongue* is indispensable in the erotic kiss; and 'plays lead' in its most important variations. This may take the form of vigorous and pronounced penetration, but in a much more subtly differentiated manner than among the primitive peasantry of the Vendée. Indeed, the tongue-kiss is most captivating when the tip of the tongue very lightly and gently titillates the beloved's tongue and lips." (T. H. Van de Velde. *Ideal Marriage*, 1939, Heinemann, London.)

Three senses are involved in these erotic kisses—touch, taste and smell, and the last two are of particular importance. There is an undeniable difference in the flavour of the kisses of different individuals and even of the same individual on different occasions, a difference which is indescribable but perceptible to the sense of taste. Love-play usually starts with an erotic kiss between mouth and mouth, but later the kisses are transferred to the body and particularly to those areas of the body known as erogenous zones. Here the sense of smell also comes into action and, as has previously been pointed out, the sense of smell is particularly closely linked with the emotions. Kisses on various parts of the body can be looked upon as being the human version of the sniffing and smelling practices which play so large a part in the love-making of animals.

Strange to say, teeth may also enter into human love-play as they do into the love-play of animals. Erotic kisses are liable to change gradually into playful biting as excitement mounts towards the culmination of the first phase of love-making. There is nothing at all abnormal in the infliction of a gentle nibble or bite, which is insufficient to break the skin. But can the same be said if the real love-bite is so forceful as to draw blood? Dr. Van de Velde discusses this subject judicially in his book, and gives his verdict that even the drawing of a small amount of blood may be accepted as normal. But he adds that it is difficult to decide where the frontier between the normal and the pathological lies. "As in all departments of emotional life, the stages from the normal to the morbid, from the intense to the bizarre are so gradual that they can hardly be delineated by any hard and fast frontier. Does not every lover prove himself, in a sense, 'as one of unsound mind', whose aim is abnormally limited, whose field of vision is absurdly narrow? And yet there must be some rule, some guiding sign, some boundary! And I think we are justified in drawing the line, both in the love-bite and wheresoever else sexual pleasure is stirred at the infliction or endurance of pain (bodily or psychic), and drawing it clearly and firmly at the first sign of cruelty".

Women are more addicted to love-biting than are men and it is by no means unusual for a woman of a passionate nature to leave a momento of sexual union in the shape of an imprint of teeth on her male partner's shoulder. This bite is almost always inflicted towards the climax of intercourse or immediately afterwards. The bite of the male partner is usually a gentler one given during the course of love-play.

Van de Velde sums up his own feelings on the subject of the infliction of pain either by biting or by pinching during sexual intercourse as follows: "What both man and woman, driven by an obscure primitive urge, wish to feel in the sexual act, is the essential force of *maleness*, which expresses itself in a sort of violent and absolute *possession* of the woman. And so both of them can and do exult in a certain degree of male aggression and dominance—whether actual or apparent—which proclaims this essential force. Hence the sharp gripping and pinching of the arms and sides and *nates*. Hence too, the significant fact that the masculine erotic manifestation belongs to the moment of coitus itself and not to its preliminaries."

Love-play expresses itself not only in kisses and playful bites and pinchings but in touches and caresses which range in intensity from the gentlest stroking with the fingers up to gripping and pressing with the fingers together. The gentler forms of caressing are usually the most effective and the areas which arouse the greatest response in the passive partner are usually the various erogenous zones of the body. But the responses to gentle tactile movements of this kind are different in different individuals and it will be for the lovers to explore and to study each other's idiosyncrasies in this matter of tactile sensibility.

There exist no rules and bye-laws either in love-play or in the sexual intercourse to follow it beyond the laws reached by the lovers by mutual and often by unspoken agreement. Whatever is pleasing, aesthetic and satisfying to both lovers is right and proper; whatever is mutually displeasing and unaesthetic is wrong. Love creates its own values and has its own code of ethics and this is of far more importance than anything spoken or written by others on this subject. A husband is soon able to sense what pleases his wife even though no words have passed between them, for with one kind of action she tends to withdraw from him and with another she advances to meet him with signs that it is pleasing to her. It is quite likely that at first he may be handicapped in judging what is agreeable to his wife by the fact that the love-act is taking place in the dark, so that he is unable to see her expression, but through touch and movements alone he can usually tell what is and what is not pleasing to her.

All writers on this subject advise those who are beginners in the art of love-making to devote a considerable time to to kisses and manual caresses, before the genitals are touched. But eventually the gentle strokings should reach the abdomen and the inner aspects of the thighs. The fingers then may touch the female sexual organs and pass on again to the other thigh. These caresses will probably have two results; first, the wife's thighs will separate slightly and automatically, so as to render her genital organs more accessible and second, the increased blood supply to the external folds of the vulva will cause them to expand. When this stage has been reached the clitoris, the most highly erogenous structure in the whole of the female body, can be lightly stroked. This still further increases the woman's sexual excitement and her desire, but the husband's touch must be extremely gentle for the clitoris is very richly supplied with nerves and is consequently exquisitely sensitive.

Love-play is not what some people are inclined to believe it to be, an artificial elaboration of the sexual act invented by sensualists, but it is a physiological requirement, the means by which certain physical changes are brought about in the vagina or female passage. These changes are a necessary preliminary to the entry of the male organ of sex, the phallus or penis. During the whole of this period of love-play secretions of a lubricating nature are being poured out by a number of glands in the skin folds of the vulva and at the same time the female passages are being opened out through the engorgement of the spongy erectile tissue contained in their walls. Unless the woman has been properly prepared in this way, intercourse will cause her discomfort and penetration will be both difficult and painful. For this reason husbands who have acquired experience in erotic technique, never cut short this preliminary stage of love-making, knowing as they do that until it has been completed their partner will be unable to derive full satisfaction from the next phase of intercourse. The existence of moisture at the entrance to the vagina and in the neighbourhood of the clitoris are signs that the preliminary stage of love-making has been satisfactorily completed and that the next stage can begin.

It is at this critical point of intercourse that the active help of the wife will be required for it is difficult or impossible for a husband to find his way unaided into the female passage. What therefore is needed is that she should take the male organ in her hands and guide it in the required direction, shifting her own body, or that of her husband, whenever it is necessary to do so in order to obtain the right alignment. It is at this stage of intercourse that the earlier attempts of a newly married couple are most likely to come to grief. Not realizing that her husband requires her help, the inexperienced wife lies there passive and leaving everything to him, and alone he may be unable to find his way into the vagina. Not a few husbands have returned from their honeymoon despondent and convinced that they were impotent when all that was really wrong with them was that they had failed to obtain from their wives the help they required at a critical moment in sexual intercourse. Sometimes doubt is felt whether or not penetration has actually occurred, but there should be no difficulty in deciding this point. The vagina is a highly contractile organ, the walls of which contain a large amount of muscular tissue and when the vagina is stimulated it contracts automatically so as to grasp anything within its cavity. The word vagina is the Latin word for a sheath and this aptly describes its action on the male organ or phallus. Both the woman and the man should be able to state quite definitely whether penetration has happened or not.

At the entrance to the vagina lies a tiny fold of skin known as the maidenhead or hymen, a structure which has to be stretched or even torn before the marriage is consummated. The fold lies between the urethra or passage to the bladder in front and the outlet of the large bowel behind and it is protected from external injury by the much thicker folds of skin constituting the vulva. Because of the hymen's close connexion with the act of consummation it has been given great legal and symbolic importance and the pain associated with its stretching or rupture has also been grossly over-emphasized. Usually the hymen yields very easily to light pressure but as its thickness and completeness is very variable the resistance which it offers to penetration differs markedly in different cases. One of the advantages attached to a pre-marital medical examination of the woman is that it allows of the resistance of the hymen to penetration being estimated and also permits of dilatation being carried out, if this is thought to be desirable. When the obstruction is considerable the dilatation will probably be done by a doctor under an anaesthetic, but if it is comparatively small the patient may manage it for herself either by means of her fingers smeared with a little vaseline or else with the aid of a small dilator.

Sometimes the stretching of the hymen during the honeymoon is more difficult than it was expected to be but the commonest cause of a husband's failure to achieve this task is due not so much to the mechanical resistance offered by the hymen as to his fear of hurting his wife. As has already been said, far too much stress has been laid on that particular moment in the first intercourse to which the name "rupture of the hymen" has been given. The word "rupture" carries with it a threat and the anxiety felt by an apprehensive husband lest he should be too brutal and injure his wife is sometimes so great as to inhibit all desire on his part for intercourse. Too much has been made of this moment in the first intercourse and a worried husband should take comfort from the following statistics which refer to the pain experienced by brides on their first night. When a group of a hundred women were questioned on this subject of their first sexual intercourse sixty-two of them replied that they had suffered nothing beyond a mild discomfort, thirty-seven said that the first penetration gave rise to a momentary pain and only seventeen considered that the pain they had suffered could be put under the heading "severe."

The amount of distress occasioned by the first penetration will depend on two things, the toughness and tightness of the hymen and the gradualness with which dilatation is carried out. Dilatation prior to marriage is the remedy for the first condition if the state of affairs has been discovered in time and gentleness and patience on the part of the husband is the right remedy for the second. If he has the patience and the restraint to look upon the first few sexual relationships with his wife as being no more than preliminary dilatations for the complete intercourse to follow, then the difficulties will easily be overcome. During these preliminary dilatations artificial lubricants such as vaseline will have to be used because the amount of natural secretions formed by her lubricating glands will not be sufficient to make entry easy. Later when the wife's sexuality is more fully awake and both she and her husband are more experienced in lovemaking it will be possible to discard all artificial lubricants. Vaseline has the disadvantage that it is insoluble in water. This means that it cannot readily be washed away afterwards and for this reason certain water-soluble vegetable preparations such as emulsions of tragacanth are preferred by some people.

The hymen is not usually a very vascular structure and bleeding from it is trifling when it has been ruptured rather than stretched. If, in an exceptional case, bleeding is more copious it will soon stop when pressure is applied to the bleeding point by means of a pad of cotton wool or a pad made out of a handkerchief.

Dr. Havelock Ellis has shown in his *Studies in Psychology* that an element of pain may even be a desirable ingredient in the first experience of sexual passion and that it adds rather than detracts to its value for both parties. "We have to admit", he writes, "that a certain pleasure in manifesting his power over a woman by inflicting pain upon her is an outcome and survival of the primitive process of courtship, and an almost or quite normal constituent of the sexual impulse in man. But it must be at once added that in the normal, well-balanced and well-conditioned man, this constituent of the sexual impulse, when present, is always held in check.

When the normal man inflicts, or feels the impulse to inflict, some degree of physical pain on the woman he loves, he can scarcely be said to be moved by cruelty. He feels, more or less obscurely, that the pain he inflicts, or desires to inflict, is really a part of his love, and, moreover, that it is not really resented by the woman on whom it is inflicted. He is persuaded that the physical force, the teasing and bullying, which he may be moved to exert under the stress of sexual excitement are not really unwelcome to the object of his love.

Moreover, we have to bear in mind—a very significant fact from more than one point of view—that the normal manifestations of a woman's sexual pleasure are exceedingly like those of pain. "The outward manifestations of pain" declares a lady writer; "tears, cries, etc., which are laid stress on, to prove the cruelty of the person who inflicts it, are not so different from those of a woman in the ecstasy of passion when she implores the man to desist, though that is really the last thing that she desires." If a man is convinced that he is causing real and unmitigated pain, he becomes repentant at once. If this is not the case he must either be regarded as a radically abnormal person, or as carried way by passion to the point of temporary insanity.

The close association between pain and passion imparts meaning also to the drawing of blood by the love-bite and to the minor savaging which one partner may inflict on the other when borne high on a flood of passion. It is also the explanation of such grosser sexual deviations as sadism and masochism, minor degrees of which are to be found in quite a large number of ordinary people. Although Kraft Ebing is entirely right in stating that the more marked degrees of sexual deviation are to be found only in the male it is also true that minor degrees of them, and in particular minor degrees of masochism crop up in the female.

Caresses are not abandoned abruptly when penetration has been effected but are continued throughout the second and more active phase of intercourse. The most usual position for intercourse and the position which comes most naturally to a newly-married couple is that in which the woman lies on her back with her knees drawn up and with her thighs widely separated. The husband, whose body is above her and between her legs, supports his weight as much as he can on his elbows so as to avoid pressing unduly on her. When penetration has taken place, his arm curls round her back, to lend support to her shoulder and also in order to press her more closely to him.

When movements begin they should start very gently and slowly and in the earlier days of the honeymoon they are likely to be made more by the husband than the wife. Again the key to success is gentleness and absence of all hurry for the aim of the husband is to prolong this phase of the intercourse as much as possible in order to give his wife time to obtain full satisfaction, ending in an orgasm. To postpone his own climax the intensity of his sensations have to be damped down by his pausing every now and then and waiting until the feeling of imminent ejaculation has passed; then he gently resumes the movements until it is advisable for him to stop again.

One writer on the subject of sexual intercourse has compared it to a race in which two runners start at the same moment with the avowed aim of reaching the goal at the same time, but as the man is by nature the faster runner he is compelled to reduce his pace from time to time or even to wait for a moment or two in order that his partner may be able to catch up with him. Only when the finishing post comes into sight and they draw very near to it does the faster runner abandon all his previous restraint and allow his natural desire to take full possession of him. The simile is a satisfactory one provided that the word "race" does not conjure up the idea of two people striving to reach the finish as quickly as possible.

Whilst the husband is controlling his movements he is also taking careful note of what excites and gives pleasure to his wife and what does not assist her in this way. For example, some women obtain greater satisfaction from deep penetration of the vagina, whilst others are more likely to obtain an orgasm from less deep penetration where the male organ comes into closer relationship with the clitoris. Since an orgasm is brought about in woman by two things, intense genital stimulation associated with equally strong emotions it is of great importance that the husband should find out what particular variety of genital stimulation gives his wife most gratification, his aim being that both he and his partner should reach the climax at more or less the same moment. It was previously said that love-play, including tactile excitation of the clitoris should continue during the whole of the second phase of intercourse and this the husband tries to bring about by pressing himself against his wife's pubis and thus exercising a stimulating action on the highly erogenous region of the clitoris. Should it happen, as is very likely to happen at the beginning of married life, that he has attained his goal too soon, then by resuming the gentle rhythmic stimulation of the clitoris with his finger he may be able to give her the orgasm which she has previously missed.

It makes a great difference to this second and more vigorous phase of intercourse whether the previous love-play stage has been satisfactorily carried out or not. If this preliminary stage has been hurried or unskilfully performed then the second phase will almost certainly suffer as the result of it and not only will the wife fail to attain an orgasm but the whole love-act will have been deprived of what is its chief merit and pleasure, that it is a source of mutual enjoyment. For there can be no doubt that intercourse only attains its highest level when both partners are in love with each other and when both derive from it the maximum of enjoyment.

From the climax sexual union passes gently into the epilogue or after-glow and the more gradual is this transition from the second to the final stage of intercourse the better. For this reason the male organ should not be abruptly removed after ejaculation has taken place but should be allowed to remain where it is within the vagina until it has returned to its resting state, when it slips out quite naturally. Now just as a great many men tend to pay too little attention to the all-important initial phase of the act, so also are many disposed to cut short its final stage. Having obtained the satisfaction they required for themselves and having met, so far as it has been possible for them to do so, the needs of their partners they kiss their wives, bid them good-night, roll over on to their side and go to sleep. Admittedly it is quite natural for them to do this for sexual intercourse brings about intense muscular relaxation and this in turn induces sleep but by doing it they deprive both themselves and their wives of the emotional glow and of the endearing words which should bring to a fitting close their shared experience of love. Husbands should remember that for women sexual intercourse is far more than a physical act and many wives are disappointed and upset by an abrupt and matter-of-fact ending to what for them has been a deeply emotional experience.

Like its prelude courtship, love-making is capable of a great many variations and all of these variations are legitimate provided that they are pleasing to both parties. As has already been stressed there is no standard pattern of sexual behaviour so that it is impossible to draw any sharp line between what can be accepted as normal sexual intercourse and what has to be looked upon as being perverse. But because some people enjoy rules and ask for guidance on this subject, I propose to make use of the definition of the normal in love-making which has been given by the Dutch sexologist, Dr. Van de Velde. He defines the normal as, "that form of intercourse which comes between two sexually mature individuals of opposite sexes; which excludes cruelty and the use of artificial means for producing voluptuous sensations; which aims directly or indirectly at the consummation of sexual satisfaction, and which, having achieved a certain degree of stimulation, concludes with ejaculation—or emission—of the semen into the vagina at the nearly simultaneous culmination of sensation—or orgasm—of both partners".

This formulation may be clumsy but it has the advantage of being both comprehensive and practical. It will be noticed that he has laid the chief emphasis on the need for satisfaction on both sides and on the exclusion from the act of all forms of cruelty and of all artificial aids to voluptuousness. It also insists on the culmination of the act in emission, an insistence with which many sexologists, including myself, will disagree.

Love-making is an art and arts cannot be learnt out of a book but only through practice and personal experience. There is indeed something distasteful and even repellent about attempts to teach something which ought to be spontaneous by means of the written word. Love-making, wrote a poet:

> "is a secret, hidden and not known,
> which one may better feel than write upon."

But all writers on the subject of marriage do not agree with this view that variations in the sexual act should be left to the lovers to discover. Amongst the sexologists who are of this opnion is Dr. Van de Velde. He writes that, "the grade and locality of stimulation are different according to the relative position of the two partners to one another", and, as a consequence of this, the sensations arising from these vary also. "Thus diversity becomes possible in the act of coitus; and as the ancient world has testified in many of its quoted aphorisms, no pleasure is possible in sustained and repeated use unless adequate variety and shades of difference are introduced into it". This being so the subject of different attitudes in intercourse is in Van de Velde's opinion one of considerable importance.

Convinced therefore of the advisability of giving help to married people with regard to the variation of the love-act, he proceeds to describe various modifications of the face to face position of intercourse which has alone been described in this chapter. Balzac includes amongst his aphorisms on love the aphorism that woman is a "harp who only yields her secrets of melody to the master who knows how to handle her". But who asks Van de Velde, "can play this delicate human harp aright unless he knows all her chords and all the tones and semitones of feeling? Only the genius—after long practice and many discords and mistakes! But, in marriage, such discords are unspeakably painful. So the husband who wants to be more than a blunderer . . . must study the harp and the art of music."

There are two main positions in love-making, the first in which the man and woman meet face to face and the second and averse position in which the woman turns her back on the man and an entry is made from behind. "I am of the opinion," writes Van de Velde, "that the first, the face-to-face position, must be considered the more natural for human beings, for this reason, that in this position the slight curvature peculiar to the copulatory organs . . . correspond with one another. This does not mean however that the averse is unnatural or physiologic-ally inferior."

Starting from these two primary positions Van de Velde derives seven different variations from them, which he describes under the following headings: (1) The usual attitude described in this chapter; (2) various extension attitudes, in which the two bodies are fully extended or stretched; (3) the position in which the woman's body is in a state of extreme flexion, her legs being lifted at right angles to her body; (4) the various equitation or astride attitudes regarded by the Roman poet, Martial, as the obvious and normal position; (5) sitting attitude, either face to face or averse; (6 and 7) lateral attitude, face to face and averse. The chief advantage of the various averse (entry from behind) attitudes is that they bring about a maximum stimulation of the forwardly-situated clitoris and thus may lead to the woman obtaining an orgasm which she might otherwise have failed to get. Van de Velde also includes in his description the various methods of intercourse in which the female partner kneels and the male partner approaches from behind and he attributes the popularity of this human mimicry of the ways of the animal world to the action of a deep-seated "subconscious atavistic instinct" in man.

In addition to these variations of the most usual position of the two bodies during intercourse there is a special method of love-making which merits description. I refer to a controlled method of love-making of which the first account was given about a century ago by John Noyes, a member of the American Oneida Community. The name Karezza is often applied to this controlled method of intercourse, the word "Karezza" being an American-Indian word signifying "renunciation". What has to be renounced by the husband in this form of intercourse is the final act of ejaculation. Van de Velde has condemned both Karezza and the similar method known as Coitus Reservatus, on the grounds that they leave the genital organs of the male in a state of congestion and also fail to relieve sexual tension in as satisfactory a way as ejaculation relieves it. Personally, I am of the opinion that these techniques of intercourse possess several advantages and that the objections raised against them are only theoretical ones. They will be discussed therefore in the next chapter.

8

SEXUAL INTERCOURSE

LITTLE or nothing was said in the previous chapter about the orgasm in which the sexual act should culminate. It was to this highly emotional and exquisitely sensuous moment in intercourse that the Russian philosopher, Ouspensky, referred when he wrote the following: "Of all we know in life, only in love is there a taste of the mystical, a taste of ecstasy". The orgasm is of such special interest that something more must be said about it.

What takes place on the physical plane at the time of this vivid psychological experience will be studied first, and because we have more precise knowledge of what happens in the man than of what happens in the woman we shall begin with a description of the male orgasm. The most obvious physical manifestation of the orgasm in the male is the ejaculation of the semen by means of a series of muscular spasms occurring in the perineal muscles and also in the muscular fibres incorporated in the prostate and the seminal vesicles. These rhythmic muscular contractions are accompanied by waves of voluptuous sensation which provide a fitting climax to the pleasurable feelings which have preceded them.

But there is another much less obvious but equally important element in the orgasm which can best be compared with the sudden discharge of electricity from a Leyden jar. A Leyden jar is an electrical storage apparatus which is capable of receiving and of accommodating a considerable but also limited charge of electricity. When this maximum quantity has been reached the jar is liable to discharge itself whenever an electrical conductor is brought into its neighbourhood and this provides an excellent parallel with what is probably happening in the bodies of the two partners during the sexual act. During the earlier stages of the intercourse a steady mounting of "tension" is taking place in their respective central nervous systems, an event which corresponds with the charging of the Leyden jar.

In the man sexual feeling and sensation rises steeply during the first two stages of the act and they eventually attain so great an intensity that it is felt that any further increase of them would be unbearable. And then just at the point at which this over-stepping of what is physically and emotionally support-able seems to have occurred, there is a sudden explosion which brings about immediate satisfaction and relief. With the occurrence of the orgasm the tension in the central nervous systems of both partners then falls steeply so that the two lovers are swept down from a state of intense excitement and heightened perception into a state of relaxation and calm.

Rudolf von Urban, a well-known Viennese sexologist, who is now practicing in the United States, is of the opinion that the likening of the orgasm to the discharging of a Leyden jar is more than a convenient simile. He has studied sexual inter-course from the standpoint of an electrician and is convinced that there actually exists a difference of bio-electrical potential in the male and female bodies, so that an exchange between these two types of electricity takes place during sexual union. (R. von Urban "*Sex Perfection*" (Rider & Co.))

The data on which Dr. von Urban's conclusions are based are not altogether convincing but they are of great interest and in line with recent advances in biology. More and more interest is now being taken in the electrical phenomena of life and it will not be in the least surprising if in the next few years Dr. von

Urban's conviction that an orgasm is associated with an abrupt change in electrical potential were to be found to be correct.

It is along these same lines of a change in electrical potential that Dr. von Urban also explains the sexual satisfaction and release of tension which is brought about by the forms of intercourse mentioned in the last chapter, namely Karezza and Coitus Reservatus. As has already been said, when these techniques are employed there may be neither an ejaculation on the part of the male nor an ordinary form of orgasm on the part of the female, and yet a complete release of sexual and nervous tensions takes place with them, a release which is accompanied by great emotional and spiritual enjoyment. Rudolf von Urban explains this by postulating that after sexual contact has been maintained for a certain length of time (say half an hour) there is a flowing together of the two electrical charges of the two lovers, positive and negative respectively, with relief of all their previous sexual tension.

The psychological correlates of the orgasm are as striking, if not more striking, than its sensuous manifestations and as Ouspensky has said they may be so exalted as to include a taste of that psychological experience which is known to the mystics as a "timeless moment", a state of being which is associated with a marked change of the level of consciousness. This state of heightened consciousness and increased perception is accompanied by an overwhelming sense of existence and by such brightness and vividness of thought and feeling that the thoughts and feelings of ordinary life seem in comparison with them but poor faded things. And then having been carried up to these illuminated heights the lover sinks down in great successive sweeps of descent to the more dimly lit regions of ordinary existence, where he is no longer intoxicated with rapture but is still filled with wonder and with gratitude for what has happened to him. At that highly emotional moment of descent from the heights, laughter and tears seem equally appropriate modes of expression and because there is a strong urge in him to give some vent to his feelings, laughter or tears, or a mixture of them both, are likely to follow. This is one of the rare moments in a man's life in which his essence or the more real part of him is likely to assume charge of him so that the more artificial part of him, his personality, is compelled for the moment to take second place. This is one of the several reasons why the epilogue or after-glow of sexual union should never be scamped, for it is during this epilogue that the real and essential part of a man is able to communicate with the real and essential part of a woman.

The physical events which occur in the woman at the time of the orgasm are much less well understood than are the events occurring in the male, but contractions in her genital tract certainly constitute an important part of them. According to some authorities these muscular contractions have the action of facilitating the passage of the semen upwards towards the womb and thus aiding conception. The psychological correlates of the female orgasm are very similar to those which are linked with the male orgasm. At the lowest they take the form of a sudden intensification of voluptuous feelings and of the emotions, and at the highest they are accompanied by an alteration of consciousness and a taste of ecstasy.

Because sexual feeling is less centralized in the genital organs in a woman than it is in a man it is possible for her to experience an orgasm as the result only of the skilful caressing of her body without any penetration of the vagina having occurred and this is yet another indication of the importance to a woman of the love-play phase of sexual intercourse. Some husbands have been tempted to think that after a year or two of marriage the preliminary stage of intercourse can be shortened or even dispensed with altogether, but this is an error. Although it is quite possible that as the result of greater skill in love-play a wife can be brought much more quickly to the point at which she is ready for penetration, but a scamping of the preliminary stages of intercourse will materially reduce her chances of obtaining an orgasm. It is by his skill in love-play that a husband is able to compensate to a certain extent for the fact that he reaches the moment of orgasm far more quickly than his wife does. Consequently it should never be abandoned or too much shortened.

The majority of women find that the region of the vagina in which they obtain the maximum of sensation is not in its depths but nearer to the entrance to the vagina, in other words in the region of the clitoris. The alternative region in which the maximum of sexual sensation may be felt is in the upper reaches of the vagina and these two varieties of orgasm are known as clitoral and vaginal orgasm respectively. The clitoral orgasm is more likely to be attained first, and the deeper, and on the whole more satisfactory vaginal orgasm only later, but whilst recognizing the existence of this sequence, the hard fact has to be accepted that many women never manage to obtain the deeper vaginal orgasm however long they and their husbands strive to secure it.

Many explanations of this failure are possible. Difficulties in sexual intercourse resulting from wrong attitudes to sexuality which were acquired in childhood are as common amongst women as they are amongst men, for fear and guilt on the subject of sex are implanted as frequently into girls as into boys. Because of the strict instructions they have received as children never to finger their private parts some women retain the idea that it would be wrong and shameful ever to permit their being touched after their marriage. Yet Nature has expressly rendered these regions very sensitive and has placed them where they are for this very special purpose of eliciting sexual desire. And

of all the genital structures of a woman the most highly erogenous is that small organ the clitoris which is the female analogue of the male penis. Consequently women who have
grown up obsessed with this idea that it is injurious or sinful to
make use of what Nature has specially provided for use during
sexual intercourse are opposing natural laws of nature, which is
never a very profitable thing to do. Some women are quite
aware of this fact that by making full use of the clitoral area
they would be able to obtain completer sexual satisfaction, yet
so strong is the action of the old taboo that they are frightened
to defy it.

The following paragraph taken from Dr. Joan Malleson's
book, *Any Wife or Any Husband*, indicates the importance she
attributes to the stimulation of the clitoris. "Not all women
have their feeling in the outer area, but the majority of women
can be first roused there by gentle rhythmic movements of the
finger-tips, particularly if the parts have become moistened
before touch is applied. The husband should generally expect to
spend time awakening this wife in this way, and afterwards, if
she is the type who obtains her climax during full intercourse,
he will lead on to the completion of the act. But if she is a
woman who can only get her climax from outside he should
discover whether it suits her best to have her climax before or
after he has completed the act himself. The importance of this
matter cannot be overstressed, for failure to understand it is
responsible for an immense amount of suffering."

Medical opinion, like other modes of human thought, is subject to the swing of the pendulum of fashion and this is particularly well illustrated by the changes which have taken place in
medical thought on the subject of the female orgasm during
the last twenty years. Twenty years ago all writers on this subject announced that it was essential that *all* wives should
experience an orgasm and that when they failed to obtain this

marital right of theirs it was almost always due to the clumsiness or the ignorance of their husbands. But further investigation has shown that this was a gross over-simplification of what is in fact a rather complicated situation. It is now agreed by the majority of sexologists that it was a mistake to regard a marriage as a failure from the sexual point of view, as some writers had formerly done, merely on the grounds that the wife had seldom managed to obtain an orgasm. It was still more absurd of people to assume, as many of them did, that the husband was always responsible for this state of affairs. What had not been recognized by these older writers was the fact that many of the said wives were prevented from obtaining an orgasm owing to the persistence in them of some old fear or anxiety which dated back to childhood fears and anxieties, and which were so deeply engrained in them that no amount of skill on the part of their husbands could possibly overcome them.

It is because some of these old text-books are still in circulation that one occasionally hears a wife blaming her husband for being such a poor lover, thereby implying, although not actually stating it in words, that somebody else would have managed things very much better. Now, if there is anything likely to increase marriage difficulties it is that a wife should blame her husband for whatever happens to be unsatisfactory on the sexual side of their marriage. The majority of men are particularly touchy on the subject of their sexual powers and even if it be true that they are unskilful lovers, they bitterly resent any criticism on this score. If questions of sexual technique have to be discussed with unskilful husbands, it should be done very carefully and preferably by medical men. It is quite possible that such husbands are partly to blame for their wives' failure to obtain an orgasm and everything possible should of course be done to improve their sexual technique. Nevertheless it has to be borne in mind that from a quarter to a third of all wives are unable to obtain an orgasm not because of their husbands' lack of skill, but because of inhibiting factors within themselves. Some women are aware of this fact that there is something in themselves which is holding them back from obtaining what they want but they attribute their disability to something being wrong with their wombs or with their ductless glands, and not with their thinking. Their diagnosis is incorrect for it is only very rarely that a failure to obtain an orgasm is due to a physical cause in either sex. The explanation is almost always a psychological one but this subject will have to be dealt with much more fully in a later chapter.

Medical men are frequently asked how often intercourse should take place, or sometimes the question is framed in an enquiry as to whether a certain stated frequency is excessive and likely to be injurious to health. No general answer can be given to questions of this kind, for individuals vary very widely with regard both to their sexual needs and to their sexual capacities; what would be too much for one person might well be insufficient for the sexual requirements of another person. The strength of sexuality differs very markedly in different people, a variability which probably depends on three factors, the endocrine pattern of the individual in question, his psychological type and his upbringing. The only rule that can be laid down for the guidance of people is that love-making should always be sincere, spontaneous and genuine, and by this description I mean that it should never be resorted to for such extraneous motives as display or a desire to maintain a reputation for great virility. The only reason for sexual intercourse which is a fully justifiable reason is that both partners should desire it. Experience can answer better than can any doctor the question: "How often should love-making take place?"

Natural and spontaneous sexual activity has a beneficial effect both on mind and body. As the tone of the muscles is improved by exercising them, as the organs of the body are more likely to be in a satisfactory state if they are doing their appropriate work, so also are the sexual organs the better for occasional activity. It is noticeable that men frequently put on weight after their marriage, a change which cannot always be accounted for by their being better fed. So also are many feminine troubles, such as painful and irregular menstruation, improved by a satisfactory marriage. More people suffer than is realized from the forcible suppression of their sexual function and all of these sexually starved individuals are likely to benefit from marriage. As Renan once remarked, chastity is an artificial state of which Dame Nature has a low opinion.

During the honeymoon the frequency of intercourse is likely to be excessive, for curiosity and novelty impart to it an extra fillip. But full intercourse followed by emission entails the expenditure of a great deal of nervous energy on the part of the man and it is as well that husbands should realize this and should avoid establishing standards of frequency which they will be unable to maintain later on. Fortunately Nature has placed her own check on male excesses and on the establishment of fictitious standards of virility, for whereas a woman can submit to intercourse whether she desires it at that moment or not, a man is much more dependent on the possession of genuine desire. Unless he really desires and feels the need for intercourse it will in all probability be impossible for him to have it.

So also is it necessary for both partners in the marriage to accept the fact that sexual passion is an individual endowment and that no partner is able to give to the other more of it than he or she actually possesses. In the majority of marriages the strength of desire in the two partners is unequal, so that one of them is more highly sexed than is the other. If all married people were to be questioned about their sexual relationship

and if an enquiry were to be made as to whether there was anything in their marriage which they would like altered, many of
them would reply that although he or she was entirely happy
and would not wish to be married to anybody else, the marriage would have been still more satisfactory if the other
partner had been a little more highly sexed. But, he or she
would add, because everything else was so perfect in their
marriage this little defect had been easily accepted. It is only exceptionally that a match is made between two partners who are
evenly balanced with regard to their sexual needs and capacities. These findings of mine are based on the questioning of a
very large number of married people.

It is well known that there is an ebb and flow of sexual desire
both in the man and in the woman, a sexual rhythm which
varies widely in different individuals and which is related to
sexual capacity. This helps to explain what has just been
stressed that the frequency of intercourse varies greatly in
different couples and that no standard frequency can be
established for it. All that we can talk about is the average
frequency found in the study of the sexual behaviour of a very
large number of couples. A study of this kind shows that during
the first few years of their married life, if they are young, the
average frequency works out at about three or four times a
week but that as time passes and the thirties are reached the
frequency sinks to about twice a week and in the forties to about
once a week. These figures are based only on impressions and
not on statistics.

The rhythm of desire in women is closely related to the
menstrual cycle but the precise form this relationship takes is
never constant. Dr. Joan Malleson writes on this subject as
follows: "The more normal women possibly have their increase at the time likely for conception—that is, some fifteen
days before the period is due to come; some experience desire

especially before menstruation, when they are usually in their most irritable mood; and others experience it during or just after the period, which also is an unlikely time for conception. The wise husband takes notice of such variations, and as one patient lucidly explained to me, 'cashes in'."

Something has to be said about sexual intercourse during the menstrual period, for there are some women who are particularly desirous of it at about that time. The sole objection to intercourse during the menstrual flow is an aesthetic one and by adopting suitable hygienic measures, supplemented if necessary by gentle douching, this aesthetic objection can be reduced to a minimum. This reassurance that there is no medical reason why love-making should not happen then will be useful to couples who are separated a great deal owing to their husband's occupation. It is true that certain religious teachings, notably the Jewish one, strictly forbids it, but it is likely that the Hebrew doctrine was originally derived from a still older superstition about the magical properties of the menstrual flow. For all sorts of curious beliefs and customs exist in primitive races about this rhythmic phenomena in women and about the properties of the menstrual discharges.

Just as there is a great variability in the strength of sexuality in different individuals so also is there a great variability in its duration. There are men who have lost all sexual desire and in consequence of this have ceased to have sexual intercourse with their wives by the time they have reached the fifties, whilst there are others who remain potent up into the eighties. The poet Goethe is an excellent example of sexual vigour in advanced years. At the age of sixty-five he fell so desperately in love with Ulrique, a girl of nineteen, that when she rejected his suit he wrote: "I am lost in unconquerable desire. There is nothing left but flowing tears. Let them flow, let them flow unceasingly, but they can never extinguish the fire which burns me." This retention of sexuality at an advanced age seems to be a characteristic feature of many poets, musicians and artists, who have been able not only to make love up till the end of their lives, but also to create works of art. Victor Hugo was as potent as Goethe in old age, for he had an ardent affair with the young actress Sarah Bernhardt when he was well advanced in the seventies. But Sophocles, the great Greek poet and friend of Socrates, developed an entirely different attitude to love in the later years of his life, an attitude which provides us with an interesting contrast to the points of view of Goethe and Victor Hugo. When asked if he were still capable of enjoying the love of women he promptly replied; "I am only too glad to be free of it; it is like escaping from a thousand wild and savage masters."

Sophocles' sexual philosophy is one that many elderly men would do well to adopt, for elderly men are often unduly disturbed by the entirely natural decline in their sexual capacity. Their distress is usually due to their imagining that sexual capacity is a measuring rod for age, for just as there is a tendency to measure manliness in terms of virility, so also is there a tendency to equate the loss of sexual desire with the onset of senility. Yet there are decrepit old men who still retain some tattered shreds of sexuality and there are well preserved and hale and hearty old men who have long lost all sexual desire. It is an error to measure years in terms of virility. So also is it an error to imagine that the duration of sexuality can be artificially prolonged by any form of medical treatment. All that can be said on this subject is that if an elderly man wishes to retain his sexual powers as long as possible he should continue to use them and should carefully avoid all long spells of continence. It is as difficult to restart in an elderly man a function which has for long time been allowed to remain in abeyance as it is difficult to restart the engine of a long disused car.

The sexual life of woman does not necessarily come to an end with the arrival of that troublesome period of her life known variously as the menopause, the climacteric, and the change of life, for a woman may still retain an interest in the opposite sex and a desire for sexual intercourse, even although the former motive for it, the desire for a child, has disappeared. But the menopause is associated with certain changes of a regressive or involutionary nature in the female genitalia and also with the occurrence of certain emotional disturbances which, although temporary, may be very upsetting. The realization that she has reached the end of her reproductive life and that she is losing her capacity to excite love and admiration in the opposite sex may have a depressing effect on a woman. But to imagine as some women do that they have lost all charm after the change of life has taken place is complete nonsense. Let me quote from a gallant writer on this subject, W. J. Fielding, who writes: "Amongst countless numbers of women the climacteric has been the beginning of a golden period of achievement. Nor is there any reason why women normally constituted should lose their sexual charms at such a time. As a matter of fact many women are more attractive at fifty than they were at twenty-five and if their personality has been developed and enriched by the passing of the years, they may be more charming at sixty than they were at thirty."

The menopause is associated with and is initiated by certain changes in the endocrine glands and it would be a mistake to gloss over its difficulties. For many women the menopause is a very disturbing period of life, marked by both physical and psychological difficulties. Novelists are well acquainted with the emotional distresses associated with it, and the dangerous age of woman, has provided them with useful material for their books.

Some women experience a temporary heightening of desire at

the climacteric and if they are married, their husbands may not be able to satisfy them. Should they be unmarried or should they fail to find sexual satisfaction at home they may turn elsewhere for it, and often in the direction of men much younger than themselves.

Whether or not a comparable period occurs in men also is a debatable question, but it is quite likely that there is, and that the enlarged prostate, exhibitionism and park offences are amongst its symptoms. In ancient days a "grand climacteric" for man was recognized by the Arabian School of Medicine and it was placed at an age at which prostatic enlargement often begins.

Whether we believe in a male climacteric or not there can be little doubt that about this time in a man's life there occur symptoms both physical or psychological which are very similar to the symptoms occurring in women at a somewhat earlier age.

9

CONTROLLED FORMS OF
LOVE-MAKING

SOME people look upon food merely as so much material by means of which hunger is relieved and on eating, not as a pleasure to be lingered over, to be savoured and to be enjoyed, but only as a method of satisfying the needs of the body. So also are there many men and women who regard sexual intercourse only as the means of relieving the sexual hunger to which the body is periodically subject, an activity which is enjoyable so long as it lasts, but unfortunately it lasts only a very short time. So fleeting a pleasure is sexual intercourse to some men that it is over almost as soon as it has begun, far too quickly indeed to allow of their partners reaching a climax of orgasm.

Most couples accept the fact that the pleasures of love-making are short-lived as unalterable, and after the excesses of the first six months of marriage they settle down to a routine pattern of love-making which shows few variations year in and year out. They become as conventional in their love-making, as they are conventional in all their other activities. A few couples are more enterprising and they may discover in course of time that by making certain modifications in their original technique of love-making they are able to prolong its duration. Everything has to be paid for and it is true that some of the intensity of excitement and sensation which was previously obtained from sexual intercourse has had to be sacrificed in order to make it last longer, but they find this to be a very small payment for what they have gained. In order to understand

the method by which the duration of intercourse can sometimes be increased something has to be said about the physiology
of sexual intercourse in the male.

The two nerve centres which control the activity of love-
making in the male are situated in the lower third of the spinal
cord and they are known as the erection centre and the ejaculation centre respectively. These two terms are self-explanatory,
the erection centre playing the leading role during the first
stage of intercourse and the ejaculatory centre taking over the
management in the final stage of it.

What actually happens in the central nervous system of the
man during the activity of love-making? The answer to this
question is roughly as follows. The first event is the production
of sexual excitement in the cerebral hemispheres of the brain
brought about by the presence of a sexually attractive female
and the arising in the mind of erotic thoughts. This increasing
excitement in the mind sends nerve impulses down certain
nerve fibres in the spinal cord to the erection centre and from
there they are carried onwards to the male genital organs. As
the result of these messages the phallus or male organ becomes
engorged with blood and erect. The second and more active
phase of intercourse then begins and during the whole of it the
erection is maintained by two means; by the constant arrival
of messages at the erection centre from the increasing area of
excitement in the brain, and also from the very intense sensations reaching it from the male genital organ. The charge of
nervous impulses accumulating in the erection centre from
these two regions eventually become so overwhelming that the
centre is unable to retain them any longer, and, as when a river
is in flood, the nervous tension bursts through the boundaries
of the erection centre and excites also the neighbouring ejaculation centre, thus bringing about ejaculation and the end of
sexual intercourse.

The explanation of that very common male complaint, a premature emission of semen, is that this flooding over of nervous impulse from the erection centre into the ejaculation centre takes place far too quickly. Indeed, it may be said that in civilized man the erection centre is rarely able to retain its charge of nervous impulse sufficiently long for satisfactory intercourse to take place unless appropriate steps are taken to secure this retention of it, and as was said at the beginning of this chapter, the appropriate steps are to reduce, from time to time, the intensity of the nervous impulses reaching the over-burdened centre.

This is done by a process which is best described as a "putting down of the soft pedal", on the two routes by which the impulses are reaching the centre. When the male partner begins to feel that his sensations are becoming so intense that the emission reflex is imminent, he deliberately reduces the sensations in his genital organ by stopping for the time being all movements, resuming them only when the feeling that he is about to ejaculate has subsided. This may be regarded as "putting down the soft pedal" on the sensual impulses reaching the erection centre from the male organ. "Putting down the pedal" on the nervous impulses reaching the centre from the brain is effected by deliberately reducing the intensity of sexual excitement. This is achieved by diverting the attention, for example, by watching the breathing or by counting. A husband who has become an expert in this method of soft-pedalling is able to continue intercourse for as long as may be required for his wife to obtain complete satisfaction. When he feels that her needs have been met, he abandons all artificial restraint and allows the natural and uninhibited mechanism of intercourse to come into play.

It is only when the husband starts from the normal level of efficiency that he is able to become an adept in this control technique. Should his emission reflex be so premature that it comes into action almost immediately after penetration he will be too heavily penalized to allow of his putting into practice the methods which have been described above. Before any control will be possible for such a husband it will be necessary for him to have medical, and in all likelihood psychiatric, treatment, for his special difficulties.

Having learnt something about the physiology of sexual intercourse in the male the reader will now be in a much better position to understand the method of coitus known as Karezza or Coitus Reservatus, to which reference was made in a previous chapter. This special technique was and still is practised by a certain American social and religious body known as the Oneida Community, and it was originally introduced for purposes of birth control. Because of its many advantages it was later adopted for other reasons also. Dr. Dickinson describes the method as consisting of prolonged intercourse accompanied by maximum and varied excitement, with orgasm for the woman if desired; with no seminal emission—or rare external emission—but with the substitution of a gradual subsidence of feeling for the man.

Dr. Alice Stockman has devoted a whole book entitled *Karezza* to this subject and she describes and comments on this method of love-making as follows. She starts by saying that it leads to a state of spiritual exultation in both partners by increasing the spiritual elements in the love-making at the expense of the purely sensuous elements. She writes: "The caresses lead up to connexion and the sexes unite quietly and closely. Once the necessary control has been acquired, the two beings are fused and reach sublime spiritual joy. This union can be accompanied by slow controlled motions, for soft sensations. If there is no desire to procreate, the storming violence of the orgasm will thus be avoided."

According to this writer those who are experts in the

Karezza technique are able to enjoy sexual communion for an hour or more and they obtain from it complete satisfaction, although no emission or orgasm has occurred.

A number of objections have been brought by medical authorities against this method of intercourse, such as that it leaves the reproductive organs of the male in a state of congestion instead of in the state of rest brought about by an emission. It has even been stated that it may lead to a condition of impotence. In my opinion these objections are theoretical armchair objections, rather than practical ones. To suggest that controlled intercourse is likely to produce impotence is entirely ridiculous.

As will be easily understood the employment of Karezza requires a considerable amount of control on the part of the male partner and no weakly sexed man, or man who experiences difficulty in intercourse should, or can attempt to use it. I would go so far as to say that Karezza would be more likely to act as a method of treatment for the particular form of impotence which is associated with premature ejaculation, than to be a cause of it. The fact that the Oneida Community has grown into a group of some two thousand people and that the level of health, both physical and mental, in the community is remarkably high, does not suggest that the objections brought by certain medical critics against the practice of Coitus Reservatus need be taken very seriously.

Another criticism of this technique of intercourse is that it is beyond the reach of the majority of couples. Again I am inclined to doubt this verdict on Coitus Reservatus. Eastern races have directed far more attention to the project of prolonging the sexual act than have Western people and through much practice a great many Eastern couples have obtained what they desired. The Eastern husband is usually very proud of his achievements in the way of control, not merely because it adds to his own sexual pleasure but because it gives completer satisfaction to his wife. And it is undoubtedly true that the less tempestuous and more prolonged type of intercourse known as Karezza is particularly well suited to the requirements of the female partner. As was previously said a woman's sexuality is much more closely linked with her emotions than is the sexuality of a man. She is less able than he is to love with the body alone but desires instead to bring into the union the whole of her being. Because of this the gentler form of intercourse in Karezza and the knowledge that her husband is deliberately holding his passion in check for her sake makes a special appeal.

As Dr. Eustace Chesser has put it: "Love to a woman is her whole existence, something inseparable from her other thoughts, activities and life goal. Only when her deepest nature is thus touched and brought into the sex act, can genuine union result. And when this is achieved, the wife's deepest emotional and spiritual being is so intensely stirred that a sense of spiritual exultation is experienced. Here we approach the highest attainable joys which marriage can yield. Some modern exponents of the enlightened Christian view of marriage insist that, at best, the sex episode should be of a sacramental nature. They maintain that the coming together in the physical embrace should be the outward and visible sign of the love which each partner feels for the other—the act which symbolizes their devotion. Does any form of physical union express this better than Karezza? That it takes time, patience and a great deal of mutual effort directed towards happy adjustment, is an argument for prolonged intercourse, not against it. It would be an advantage if young couples would take the sound advice given by the Rev. David R. Mace, that they should regard, say, the first five years of marriage as a sort of novitiate, during which they would think of their relationship as a gradual process of gradual adaptation to each other. (Eustace Chesser *Love without Fear*, Rich & Cowan Medical Publication).

The fact that we have had to work for any success we may have attained is likely to increase the pleasure we derive from it and this is particularly true of success in love. Love which has come to us easily is usually less appreciated than love which has been reached only after many struggles and, in Karezza, obstacles have been deliberately placed in the path of a quick and easy satisfaction in order that something much more valuable to both partners should be attained. It is true, and it is also no great disadvantage, that considerably more has been demanded of the male partner than of the female partner in the way of checking natural desires and exercising restraint.

As has already been said this method of controlled intercourse admits of several variations; it may stop short of the orgasm for both partners; it may allow of an orgasm being obtained by the woman only; or it may take the form of a prolonged contact and love-play which ends in an orgasm for both partners.   It is obvious that controlled forms of intercourse are less likely to appeal to couples in the earlier than in the later years of married life, for in the earlier years passion is so strong that it is difficult to hold it in check. But in course of time the violence of sexual passion generally subsides and a gentler form of love-making takes its place, a love-making which is based more on tenderness and mutual understanding than on erotic passion. It is in these later years of married life that controlled methods are most likely to be practised and found to be of value.

Another advantage attached to controlled methods of intercourse which stop short of an orgasm for the male is that they allow of the husband having intercourse again sooner than he would otherwise have been able to have had it, which is a matter of considerable advantage if he happens to be older than his wife. The intensity of sexual desire slowly declines with age and if the discrepancy in years between the husband

and the wife be a marked one, anything which helps him to conserve his sexual powers and to meet the needs of his wife is of value to him.

It has also to be borne in mind that sexual intercourse is more fatiguing to, and demands the expenditure of, more energy in the case of the male than in that of the female. Nor is this in the least surprising that an activity which so entirely dominates a man's body and soul as sexual intercourse does should be followed by a certain amount of fatigue. It is not so much the muscular exertion which is responsible for a middle-aged husband's subsequent tiredness as the demands that have been made on his nervous system, and the higher the sexual tension, the more abrupt its ebb and the more intense the final orgasm, the greater is this expenditure of nervous energy. The fact that the final ecstasy is usually less intense in the woman and that it dies away more slowly explains why women are less exhausted by sexual communion than are their partners. It is not surprising therefore that it was a man who first uttered the well-known phrase: *Post coitus omne animal triste*—("After intercourse all animals are sad"). But energy is rapidly restored to both partners after sleep and extreme fatigue is felt by the male only when intercourse has been too frequent for him or when it has been undertaken when he was already tired by other things.

There can be no doubt that regular and satisfying intercourse has a beneficial effect on both partners and it is particularly beneficial to women who have previously suffered from dysmenorrhoea or painful disturbances of the function of menstruation. Only when sexual excitement is too prolonged or when it involves paroxysms which are repeated at too short intervals is a woman likely to suffer from lassitude or languor as the result of intercourse. The signs of sexual excesses are the same in both sexes, the most conspicuous being fatigue, headache, disinclination for mental exertion and pain in the loins and genital organs.

But although satisfied sexual intercourse is often good for a woman's health, the fact has to be accepted that many women obtain from it very little or no benefit at all. Quite a large number of women tolerate sexual intercourse only for the sake of their husbands or else because it is the means by which they can obtain children, and not because it is a rich and highly gratifying experience. So far as we can discover the truth about the sexual experience of women in marriage this has always been true of a large number of women. It is indeed quite likely that the percentage of sexually dissatisfied married women was even higher in the Victorian Age than it is at the present time. No reliable figure can be produced in support of this statement, that the incidence of sexual frigidity in the Victorian Age was higher, but there are good reasons for believing that this was so.

That many married women remain sexually dissatisfied at the present day cannot be doubted. A recent four-year study of a hundred marriages in the United States revealed the fact that no fewer than forty-six per cent. of the wives never experienced a single orgasm during the whole of the four years of observation. Very similar figures have been given for European countries. Dr. Brunner, a well-known Swiss gynaecologist, reports that fifty per cent. of Swiss wives never obtain any real satisfaction from sexual intercourse. A similar enquiry was made in 1923 amongst female students studying at Moscow University and this showed that only forty-eight per cent. of them had ever derived any real enjoyment from sexual intercourse. Dr. Eustace Chesser also states that few women in this country enjoy sexual intercourse "to the full", but he adds that, "completely frigid women are rare. Many a woman who never experiences an orgasm finds pleasurable excitement in love-play and coitus, although she is left 'high and dry', as one patient put it. They enjoy intercourse up to a point. But they are never completely satisfied."

Dr. Chesser makes another interesting point in his report on sexual satisfaction and dissatisfaction amongst married women in this country. It is that a woman who is genuinely happy, even although she rarely or never experiences an orgasm, will not have to suffer either physically or psychologically on account of her deprivation, nor, if she is clever, will her husband have to be penalized by it, for the clever wife is always capable of simulating an orgasm. I agree with this statement and I have known husbands to live with their wives for twenty or even thirty years without ever having realized that during the whole of this time their female partners in love-making have never once obtained any genuine satisfaction from it.

It is only the women who belong to Dr. Eustace Chesser's third category of wives, that is to say wives of a warm and affectionate nature, who are likely to benefit from an improvement in their husband's technique of love-making or from the adoption of the Karezza method of intercourse. For the other two groups no amount of love-play and no extension of the total duration of the intercourse will have any benefit at all. Their inhibitions are far too deep-seated to be capable of being removed in this way and in all probability attempts to give them greater sexual pleasure and to prolong the duration of the act will only make things worse.

10

SEXUAL DIFFICULTIES AND DEVIATIONS

SEXUAL intercourse is a different thing for different people; it can be a purely physical activity carried out for the relief of sexual tension; it can be a fleeting relationship between two people who are sexually attracted to each other; it can take place between two people who have a strong emotional feeling for each other as well as sexual attraction; it can be an expression of love between two people sufficiently developed emotionally and spiritually to be able to experience sexual communion at its best. Love-making on this high level is not attained at once but only as the final stage of a long journey.

Some of the earlier stages on the road to sexual maturity will have to be discussed. Freud described three of them, the auto-erotic, the homosexual, and the heterosexual stages of sexual development. Oswald Schwarz, continuing this series, speaks of three later stages of development illustrated in young men, by the stage of their commerce with prostitutes, the stage of "the affair", and finally the stage of maturity and marriage. He does not claim that all men have to pass through these periods in their sexual development but asserts only that many have to and that each step marks a distinct advance in their sexual progress. He writes: "I have tried to present a kind of slow-motion picture of sexual development. All its stages—infantile sexuality, masturbation, homosexuality, commerce with prostitutes, and 'affairs'—may appear to have been unduly drawn out, but this was necessary in order to study their features in close up. That they are real stages of an intelligible process has, I hope, been demonstrated, but whether they are also necessary steps in practice it is impossible to say. . . . No doubt many men can take all the hurdles in one great jump, and land safely and successfully in the bridal chamber, but for the majority a more pedestrian pace may be a *safer* way to the goal". (Oswald Schwarz—*The Psychology of Sex*. Pelican.)

Some readers may be surprised or even offended that Dr. Schwarz should have recommended illicit forms of love as a *safer* road, but he was a medical man with a great deal of experience of marriage difficulties, and it is undoubtedly true that from the sexual point of view marriages are safer if the husband has had previous experience of love-making. Many men marry not only in ignorance of the art of love-making but with entirely wrong attitudes to sexuality. Take, for example, a man who has grown up with the idea that sex is of a comic nature. From the very start all manifestations of sexuality have been regarded by him as excellent material for ribald stories and obscene drawings. Even now that he has grown up he continues to look upon sexuality as a theme for smoking-room stories. Is it surprising that when he marries his attitude remains the same? How can he regard any intimacies with his wife in any other light than this? Sexuality for him still remains ribald, and the more he is in love with and admires his wife, the less likely he is to be able to associate her with such obscene behaviour as love-making. As a result he may even find himself impotent with his wife and capable only of love-making with prostitutes. The following is a good example of such a case.

The patient, a naval officer of thirty, had been married for two years without being able to consummate his marriage. No organic trouble could be discovered in him but on being questioned he freely admitted that he had always found sex a "messy and disgusting business". His young wife had previously told me that she had never been able to understand why, during moments of sexual intimacy, he had always roared with laughter as though to him love-making were some ribald joke. This could be very easily explained. For him sexuality was a messy and disgusting business, and love-making was actually a ribald joke. There were also strong homosexual elements in him and the marriage was later annulled.

Sexual difficulties at the start of marriage can often be traced also to fear—fear of inflicting pain, fear of contracting venereal disease, fear of the consequences of previous masturbation, or only a vague ill-defined fear of wrong-doing. Old fears which were formerly linked with the idea of sex often reassert themselves after a man's marriage. For example, although a husband knows quite well that there exists no possibility at all of his contracting venereal disease from his wife, he may nevertheless feel anxiety on this score because venereal disease has always been closely linked in his subconscious mind with the idea of sex. Another common fear is the fear of being found wanting. The bridegroom may have read a book on sexual deviations and disorders and, like a medical student who has studied a text-book on medicine, he has applied what he has read to himself. The following case is an instance of this.

The patient, aged forty-one, first married at the age of thirty-two, and for three years he enjoyed an active and successful sexual life. His wife then died, and for five years he remained entirely continent. He then remarried and to his consternation found that he was impotent. Investigation showed that during the interval of widowerhood he had become keenly interested in Havelock Ellis's well-known work on the psychology of sex and had persuaded himself that he was suffering from certain sexual deviations. He was eventually convinced that he had made a technical error and immediately recovered his power.

Over ninety per cent. of the sexual difficulties to be met with in marriage are psychological in origin and are usually the consequence of a faulty attitude to sexuality. Deep down in the patient's mind there lurks some fear or feeling of guilt, some inhibiting factor which dates back to childhood. Although we of the twentieth century pride ourselves on possessing a much more enlightened outlook than our Victorian grandparents had, and although our children are given instruction at school on the biology of reproduction, psychiatrists are still being consulted by well-educated and intelligent young people of both sexes whose marital difficulties are entirely the result of their early introduction to the subject of sexuality. If a child has been led to believe from the behaviour as well as from the speech of the grown-ups around him that there is something highly improper, inferior, disgusting and sinful about manifestations of sexuality, these ideas are likely to persist in his or her subconscious mind into adult life. The fact that the individual in question has married has no effect on this; in the subconscious regions of the mind sexuality in all its manifestations is still improper, inferior, disgusting and sinful.

P. D. Ouspensky applies the general term infra-sex to all of these wrong attitudes to sexuality and he draws attention to the fact that in all cases of infra-sex the sexual function is divorced from everything else in the individual and particularly from the emotions, including the emotion of love. "Normal Sex", he writes, "is first of all entirely co-ordinated with other sides of man's life and with the highest manifestations. It does not stand in their way and does not take energy from them; the energy used in the functioning of normal sex is immediately replaced owing to the richness of the sensations and impressions which are received by the intellect, the consciousness and the feeling. Further, in normal sex there is nothing that can be the subject of laughter or that can be connected with anything that is negative in man. On the contrary it repels, as it were, everything that is negative, and this in spite of the very great intensity of sensation and feeling connected with it. It does not follow that a man of normal sex is free from sufferings or disappointments connected with sex life. So far from that, these sufferings may be very acute, but they are never caused by the inner discord between sex and other functions, as in the case of infra-sex. Normal sex is co-ordinated and harmonious, but life is not co-ordinated and not harmonious; therefore normal sex may often bring much suffering. But a man of normal sex does not blame other people for his sufferings and does not try to make other people suffer." (P. D. Ouspensky—*A New Model of the Universe* —London, Kegan Paul, 1938.)

Ouspensky is right in emphasizing the fact that for a man of normal sexuality love-making is as natural a method of expressing love for a woman as poetry and music. Instead of being a hostile force with which it is necessary for him to struggle, sexuality seems to him to be the normal language of love. It is quite true that a few people are called upon to sacrifice their sexuality, but such people are very exceptional. They are the great spiritual teachers of the world, men and women who are engaged in the work of transmuting the fine energy of sex into the still finer energy required for spiritual development.

It cannot be expected that love-making can be learnt within a few weeks of getting married and that everything will run smoothly at once. A husband often starts off very badly with a premature ejaculation, and the wife's initial soreness from the consummation of the marriage may be followed by a mild attack of cystitis or inflammation of the bladder. The honeymooners' earlier experience of love-making may, therefore, be very different from the love-making described in the previous chapter, but they should not be disheartened by this. Initial disappointments of this kind are very common and the inexperienced couple should remember that many others besides themselves have made a bad start. Love-making will improve with experience, or, if this does not happen, advice can be obtained on the return from the honeymoon which will help to put things right. In the meantime panic will only do harm.

There is, however, a limit to the time that should be allowed for difficulties to clear up spontaneously, and if things are not much better after four or five weeks of married life, expert advice should be sought. I have known couples wait for as long as two years before taking advice, in the hope that things would right themselves naturally. To delay as long as this makes treatment more difficult, for errors by this time have become wrong habits, and the confidence of the husband may have been completely undermined. Treatment would have been easier if the husband had sought expert advice sooner.

Something must now be said about sexual impotence and about its treatment, and for three reasons: first, that it often causes intense emotional suffering; second, that it is far commoner than is generally supposed; and third, that there is a great deal of misunderstanding on the subject. Impotence occurs only in men and this puts them at a grave disadvantage to women, who may suffer from frigidity or inability to enjoy sexual intercourse but who can always take part in it, even though they have no desire to do so. As Dr. Stafford Clark has put it, a woman can submit to intercourse when she is thinking and worrying about something else, "with her mind perhaps loaded with anxious or even guilty preoccupations of which her husband or lover may know nothing. On the other hand, a man is very rarely able to do anything like this. He cannot command his erection; it is something which happens to him when he is in a certain emotional frame of mind. Anything which prevents that frame of mind possessing him may prevent his erection. . . . Therefore in one sense the man is, so to speak, on trial in a sexual situation. It may be no good his protesting that he loves or desires his partner, if he cannot produce the physical evidence by his condition. Yet the more he worries about a possible difficulty, the more likely it becomes that this difficulty will arise. And once it has arisen, the effect both on him and his partner in terms of further guilt, anxiety and discouragement, may well reinforce the already unhappy situation which precipitated it." (Dr. D. Stafford Clark, *The Practitioner*, April 1945.)

Few men who have become impotent are able to see any connexion between their physical trouble and the emotional dilemma which has been responsible for it. And their inability to see this connexion is understandable, for quite often their impotence arises from emotional disturbances of a non-sexual nature. For example, many a man has been rendered temporarily impotent by an overbearing father who bullied him as a boy into believing that he was no good, or at any rate, markedly inferior to someone else, such as an older or a younger brother. Now when the father undermined his boy's confidence in himself in this way, the last thing he had in his mind was to render him incapable of being a husband, but quite naturally his son has applied what his father said to every field of endeavour. He has grown up hesitant and without confidence in himself, and when the time eventually comes for proving his manhood during his honeymoon, he lamentably fails. Humanity has been conditioned to look upon virility as a measure of a man's strength, and this makes the male particularly prone to attacks of psychogenic impotence.

The confirmation of the fear that he may be impotent has a devastating effect on a husband. He is so deeply ashamed and humiliated by what has happened that he shirks taking advice on the matter. He is convinced that his impotence is incurable and he clings so tenaciously to this view of his trouble that when the expert he is eventually driven to see declares his trouble to be psychogenic and curable, he flatly refuses to believe him.

Not only does he repudiate the idea that his trouble is spychological, but he closes up like an oyster and refuses to disclose the anxieties which have given rise to his trouble. So stubborn was one patient about the cause of his impotence that I was compelled to have recourse to a trick to save him from his own folly.

The patient was a youth of twenty, brought up by a widowed mother. The word sex was never mentioned in the house, and so "modestly" was he brought up that he was never allowed to see even his sister in her dressing-gown. All signs of sexual curiosity on the part of the two children was noted by the mother, a so-called "religious" woman, with the gravest apprehension. But the boy had had his sexual curiosity satisfied at a public school and learnt there also how to masturbate. This he continued to do but with an increasing sense of guilt. Whilst indulging in this habit he felt a sharp stab of pain, and was convinced that irreparable physical damage had been done. A subsequent "trial" of sexual intercourse with a prostitute proved a failure, and now he was in a state of deep despair. Doctors were consulted, and finally he came to the author of this book. An examination showed that there was no physical justification for his fears. Realizing that the case was a desperate one and that it was quite likely that he would commit suicide if he were not cured, a new line was adopted. It was agreed that a small ligament had been torn, but it was also pointed out that nothing would be easier than to stitch the torn portions of the ligament together. After the mother had been told the truth about her son's trouble, he was taken into a nursing home and, under an anaesthetic, a small wound was made in the skin and then immediately stitched together again. Psychotherapeutic measures were started during his stay in the home, and continued after his return to his own home, and within a few weeks he was cured. All that he had required was the psychological treatment he had refused to accept from his previous medical advisers.

Some of the fears responsible for initial difficulties in marriage have been already mentioned, and a complete list would include also the following: a long-standing fear of sexuality and of all its manifestations; a fear of women in general; a fear of letting his wife down, of disappointing her, of failing to live up to her picture of him as a man, and—perhaps most common of all—the fear that by his failure he will confirm what he has always dreaded to have confirmed, that he has irretrievably damaged his sexual powers through masturbation. Guilt on the subject of masturbation is terribly widely spread and it shows us how closely linked sexuality is in the West with the primitive ideas of sin, guilt and punishment.

Much will depend on the reaction of the wife to her husband's early failures, for if she manages to take them quietly and with patience and understanding, his chances of subsequent success will be greatly increased. The wife's understanding and co-operation are also of great importance if any treatment is required. It would indeed be true to say that without the wife's help no medical treatment is likely to be of any use to him. Men are rendered particularly vulnerable by a failure to complete the sexual act, and any sign of scorn on the part of their partners inflicts wounds so deep that they may never be able to recover from them. Loss of confidence is fatal, of course, and I can still recall the manner in which an extremely able professional woman brought her own husband to see me. She sailed into the consulting room, and after bidding her obviously frightened husband to sit down and let her handle his case properly, she described to me in bitter terms, in his presence, his total inadequacy as a husband. The explanation of his impotence was obvious—it was the lady herself.

It has to be accepted that marriage demands much more of a man nowadays than it did before the education of women and the granting to them of equality. In former days a wife did not expect what the modern emancipated woman expects, and has the right to expect of marriage. She was content, or at any rate outwardly appeared to be content, to look after her husband's home and to be a good mother to his children. But now that she is her husband's equal, she expects of him sexual satisfaction and it is quite understandable why she should do so. I quote from a postscript by a psychologist to a former book of mine on the subject of marriage. "Even more important than the political, cultural or economic freedom of woman is her new emotional independence. In no sphere are greater liberties or advantages accorded men than women. Even in the most intimate domain of sex relations, woman is treated as adult with complete freedom of action." Mr. Peter Fletcher then goes on to say that he entirely agrees that emotional independence is an important requirement for a stable wife-husband relationship. His experience as a psychologist has convinced him that it is required not only for a satisfactory marriage but also for any human relationship which is grounded on friendship or love instead of expediency.

"We talk very glibly of love", he writes, "but there seems to be no general recognition that reciprocity is the very essence of it, and therefore only to the extent that we are emotionally free are we capable of giving or experiencing it."

This is quite true, but at the same time we have to accept the fact that whilst the education of women and the recognition of their equality has increased the potential richness of marriage, it has also made marriage a much more exacting task to the husband. A modern wife is much less inclined than was her predecessor to keep silent if all is not going well with the sexual side of her marriage. Being her husband's equal she is in a position, if necessary, to demand her sexual rights, but in doing so she must be very careful never to overstep the mark. Nature has ordained that man should be the dominant partner in sexual intercourse, and although a wife may take the initiative with impunity in all other spheres of activity, if she takes the lead too blatantly in the marriage bed she will find herself in possession of an impotent husband.

In the majority of marriages it comes quite naturally to the husband that he should take the lead in sexual intercourse, and the wife is only too happy that he should do so. But in a few marriages the reverse holds good and it is the wife who has been forced, even against her own womanly instincts, to become the more active partner. This reversal of rôles is more likely to happen in those marriages in which the wife, unknown to herself, is acting as a mother to her husband.

When sexual failures occur in marriage, and an occasional failure in intercourse can happen in any marriage, the partner who bears no responsibility for it may be more upset by what has happened than the responsible person. This is because he or she feels somehow to blame for the mishap, and such feelings of guilt should be strongly discouraged, for guilt and blame have no place at all in the love relationship. The more lightly such occasional failures are taken, the better for everybody. Premature ejaculation and a loss of erection are the commonest causes of failure in the male, and lack of response and painful spasm in the female. Premature ejaculation is by far the commonest sexual trouble in marriage, as the following statistics show. The American sexologist, D. J. Exner, states that out of every nine American husbands one ejaculates almost immediately, that one out of six of them is capable of sustaining intercourse for, say, two minutes, and that the remainder can continue intercourse for any time between three minutes and half-an-hour. British statistics would probably be very similar.

Men who have remained celibate up to the time of their marriage are particularly liable to have their first efforts to make love frustrated in this way, but if they and their partners accept what has happened quietly and avoid all panic, the trouble is likely to improve during the following three or four weeks. Should this improvement not occur, then the husband should seek expert advice. His difficulty will usually be found to be due to some deep seated anxiety or else to his unwillingness to commit himself entirely to the sexual act. This refusal on the part of the individual to give himself or herself whole heartedly to the partner is by no means uncommon in both sexes, and should it exist it may require expert psychiatric treatment.

The commonest sexual deficiency in the wife is an inability on her part to feel anything in the vaginal passage, a condition known medically as vaginal anaesthesia. Like the commoner disorders in the male, it is usually psychogenic in origin and not due to any physical defect in the female passage. When all feeling in the vagina is absent, little or no pleasure is obtained from sexual intercourse, and whilst some women remain permanently handicapped in this way, others may eventually manage to obtain a little feeling and pleasure from a very long and very competent intercourse. Women who suffer from this trouble will never obtain a deep-seated or vaginal orgasm, but they often manage to obtain a clitoral one. If the technique of intercourse on both sides has been rendered as adequate as it is possible to make it and yet no deep seated orgasm has ever been obtained by the wife, the couple should accept the state of affairs, for no treatment is likely to prove successful. This remark applies only to couples who have been married for a considerable time, for in the newly-wed, improvement will come as the result of greater skill in love-making.

The wives who are most in need of help are those who get fully aroused sexually but who are unable to obtain any real satisfaction from stimulation either of the vagina or of the clitoris. The only comfort that Dr. Joan Malleson can give to this not inconsiderable group of women is that they "can expect the strength of their sexual desire to lessen as time passes." It is as though Nature kindly arranges to dull feelings which can do nothing but disappoint. As a rule the best possible course is for such a woman to bear a child quite early in marriage. Even if this makes no difference to the sexual side of the marriage, the pleasure of child-bearing and new interest in family life will generally go far to counteract the nervous strain. To such a woman a large family is often the best immediate answer.

Dr. Malleson divides this group of sexually dissatisfied women into two categories, those whose sexual response depends entirely on their hope of becoming mothers, and those, on the contrary, who are terrified of becoming pregnant. To the first category of women, intercourse associated with contraceptive measures is entirely meaningless, and to the second, intercourse entailing the risk of their becoming pregnant is a nightmare. Women who are oppressed with such an abnormal fear of child-bearing as this become much happier after the change of life or after their husbands have been sterilized.

Another common obstacle to sexual adjustment is the condition known as vaginisinus, in other words, a spasm of the vagina which is so painful as to prevent penetration. A woman who suffers from this trouble does not usually realize that her pain is the result of muscular spasm but is disposed to attribute it to an overstretching of the vaginal passage. Should pain of this kind occur at the beginning of married life, it is sometimes difficult for the medical man to decide whether it is due to the mild discomfort following consummation of the marriage or whether it is a true case of vaginisinus. Like most sexual difficulties encountered in marriage, vaginisinus rarely has any physical cause and Dr. Malleson is of the opinion that the commonest explanation of it is the "soap-sticks" and enemas used previously in the treatment of such childish troubles as thread-worms and constipation. The stinging associated with these treatments is sometimes quite severe, and not knowing from what part of her body the pain is coming, a child often concludes that something is being pushed forcibly into her lower regions. These infantile memories of pain are stored up in her subconscious mind to reassert themselves many years later in resistant vaginal spasms which render the consummation of marriage difficult or impossible. Wives suffering from vaginisinus are usually very angry about the attempts being made to effect penetration, just as they were long ago angry with their mothers for torturing them with stinging enemata. The trouble can be cured by teaching the patient how to relax and how to insert dilators into her own vagina without causing herself pain.

It has been stated elsewhere that sexuality conforms to no pattern of expression, but that whatever is gratifying and without pain to both partners can be accepted as normal. But from time to time a peculiarity is revealed in the sexual desire of the husband which has to be accepted as being a deviation from normality. Should this be discovered—for in all likelihood its existence was never suspected prior to the marriage—the handicapped partner should not blame himself too bitterly for what has come to light, for the said peculiarity was none of his own contriving. Nor should he give way to despair for it is likely that he will be able to obtain help from psychiatric treatment.

The commonest deviations to be discovered are various degrees of sadism, masochism, fetishism and homosexuality. Sadism may be defined as sexual satisfaction derived from the infliction of pain on another person, and masochism as sexual emotion which is associated with the desire to be hurt or subjugated by another person. These two deviations are therefore the active and the passive forms respectively of the same preoccupation with pain; and as has clearly been shown pain has very close connexions with sexual love. This connexion is less difficult to explain than might be expected. In the first place, pain is closely linked with the sexuality of animals and of primitive man; sadism and masochism may consequently be regarded as being survivals of the time when men fought for and captured their mates. There is yet another explanation of the association of sexuality with pain. It is that humanity derives a certain perverted pleasure from the spectacle of suffering.

Lucretius was well aware of this strange fact when he wrote: "It is sweet to contemplate from the shore, the perils of the unhappy sailor struggling with death." So also do many people find it sweet to contemplate from the stalls the portrayal of the sufferings and horrors either on the stage or on the cinema screen. It is the Grand Guignol type of play or film which sells the most tickets. So it is not so remarkable that tragedy and violence add zest to the love-making of many people.

Lucian showed realism when he put into the mouth of one of his characters the following words: "He who has not rained blows on his mistress and torn her hair and her garment is not yet in love." Nor does satisfaction lie only with the aggressor in love, for Cervantes has made one of his female characters complain of her husband that, "he does not know how to make me suffer a little. One cannot love a man who does not make one suffer a little."

By the word fetishism is meant a shifting of sexual emphasis from the totality of the beloved one to some small part of her or to something closely associated with her, such as an article of clothing. Strange to say the commonest forms of fetishism revealed in the consulting room are concerned with such unlovely articles as rubber sheeting, mackintoshes and rubber gloves and here accident may be playing a predominant part. It is quite possible that the first heightening of sexual feelings may have occurred when the sufferer from fetishism was a small boy, lying on a mackintosh sheet, either in bed or on his nurse's knee. Sexual excitement has therefore become linked up in his mind with the sensation of or the idea of mackintosh. The sexual pleasure derived by some youths from the idea of being bound up with cords or from being confined, may be explained in a similar manner. Early sexual excitement may have been provoked in them when they were being dried after a bath and when their nurses at the same time deliberately restrained their movements. Sexual excitement and physical restraint became linked together in their subconscious minds.

Another cause of difficulty may be the existence of latent homosexuality in a husband, a deviation which may only be discovered after marriage. Freud taught that every individual passes through a homosexual stage in his progress towards complete sexual maturity, and the final shift from a homosexual to a hetero-sexual orientation may be delayed, or may even remain uncompleted. In the latter case the individual has to be regarded as being ambi-sexual, that is to say, as being a man who is capable of having sexual dealings with both sexes. But on careful examination it will usually be found that an ambi-sexual person derives greater pleasure from intercourse with his own sex than with the opposite sex, and, this being so, he is not likely to prove a very successful husband, so far as the sexual side of the marriage is concerned.

Some men are scarcely aware of the homosexual elements in their make-up and some realize their condition but marry nevertheless in the hope that this will cure them. Well-meaning people, relatives, clergy, and even doctors occasionally go so far as to recommend this form of treatment, assuring the patient that the influence of a good woman will resolve all his sexual difficulties. Now it is quite true that if an ambi-sexual individual makes up his mind to abandon homosexual practices for good and to banish, so far as it is possible for him to do so, all homosexual fantasies, he may make quite a good husband, but he is in honour bound to inform his future partner about his dual orientation. If she consents to marry him, well and good; but in accepting him she must also accept this fact that she may not obtain from her marriage the complete emotional and sexual satisfaction she might have obtained from marriage with a sexually mature person.

It has been repeatedly emphasized that should some difficulty arise in love-making during the honeymoon which does not right itself spontaneously within a month or two, expert advice should be taken. The family doctor is the most natural person to whom to turn for help but many people find it easier to talk about such intimate things as peculiarities in sexual desire with a complete stranger. They may even prefer the anonymity which comes from being a patient at some hospital clinic, but it is no easy matter to find the right kind of clinic. Most of the troubles discussed in this chapter demand first a physical examination, followed by a still more thorough psychological investigation but although there are excellent gynæcological and genito-urinary clinics, and equally satisfactory psychiatric clinics, there are very few, if any, combinations of them all. As the great majority of the sexual difficulties occurring in marriage are psychogenic, the first authorities to consult should be either a private psychiatrist or a psychiatric clinic. Should these authorities feel that a physical investigation is also required, arrangements can be subsequently made for this.

A great many male patients who suffer from sexual incompetence go to their doctors in the hope of being provided with an aphrodisiac which will soon put things right. This is an utterly vain hope, for mankind has been searching for easy cures of this nature ever since the dawn of history—for some magical remedy which will dispel all fears and promptly restore potency. Everything has been tried, from powdered mummy to powdered rhinoceros horn, remedies of this unusual kind being chosen on the grounds that the rarer and the more difficult the medicine is to obtain, the more likely it is to possess magical properties. No, there is no short cut to the cure of most of these cases of sexual difficulty. They will respond to treatment, but not to the kind of treatment which patients require that their doctors should give them. Patience and time are both needed and, above all, the co-operation and the understanding of the marriage partner.

Until expert advice is obtained, two things are desirable: first is that because a multiplication of failures make things worse the couple should, for the time being, give up any further attempts to have sexual intercourse. It may also be helpful for them to make a temporary change in their environment and to separate for a short time if this can be conveniently arranged. Secondly, it is of the greatest importance that they should both keep their troubles strictly to themselves and should not allow their friends and relatives to know that they are experiencing difficulties. The situation is sufficiently humiliating to the husband as it is, and if, as is quite common in Jewish families, all of the "in-laws" are to take part in the preliminary consultations, then the chances of a cure become exceeding remote.

It is a mistake to assume that a complex form of civilization necessarily entails also a high development of the arts, for this is very far from being true. Amongst the arts referred to in this statement is that Cinderella of all the arts—which is not even considered to be an art in Western lands—love-making. This very fact, that for many English-speaking people sexual intercourse is looked upon as being an instinct, is in itself a commentary on the standard of love-making in this country and in America.

Many factors contribute to the neglect of the art of love-making and to the frequency with which various forms of sexual neurosis are to be found in Western countries, and an important factor is the attitude of the Church to sexuality and to sexual problems in general. Whatever the Church may have contributed to the welfare of the other arts—and our debt to the Church in this respect is immense—its influence on our attitude to sexuality has not often been helpful.

Such ports as Corinth were centres of sexual vice and it is not surprising that St. Paul and other leaders of the early Christian Church protested so strongly against the profligacy of the age.

The net result of the early Church's negative attitude to sexuality was to establish in many people's minds a set of very dubious and arbitrary assumptions; that of all moral delinquencies, sexual errors were the most serious; that the Devil and the body, and more particularly that area of the human body responsible for reproduction, had gone into permanent partnership; that virginity and complete male chastity were highly desirable, not merely as a *means* to an end but as an *end* in themselves. As a medical man I am convinced that these blind and arbitrary rules have given rise to a great deal of inner conflict amongst those who have attempted to follow them and have loaded a great many otherwise contented people with a burden of guilt.

Fortunately the equating of sexuality with sin is less commonly found amongst the better educated people of this country than formerly but it is still productive of a great many cases of sexual neurosis. From a medical point of view a sexual neurosis can be regarded as being a conflict between a man's cerebral hemispheres and his sex centres situated in his spinal cord, as a fight between fear and a natural human function, as a contest between a taboo and the physiological requirements of the body. It is only by helping a patient to make peace between these warring elements in himself that he can be cured. This does not mean that the patient is encouraged to throw off all sexual restraint. It only means that he should realize what his situation actually is and unburden himself as much as possible of his sense of guilt. In many years of practice I have never suggested that a patient should do violence to his own conscience. All that I have asked a patient to do is to review his ideals critically and satisfy himself that they are his own ideals and not merely conventions which he has accepted blindly and without thought.

11

THE WAR OF THE SEXES

There is, and always has been, strife as well as love between the sexes, a rivalry which from time to time flares up into open warfare and then dies down again. Women have gained their liberty and are able to take up many occupations now which were formerly barred to them but even in this period of comparative peace the old rivalry between the sexes reveals itself in many different ways. It shows itself, for example, in the tacit understanding existing between the members of the same sex and their promptness to come to each other's aid. However strongly one woman may disagree with another one, she is always her ally when it comes to a joust with the opposite sex. A similar *esprit de corps* exists amongst males and a man who is telling stories about the vagaries of women at his club can always count on a loyal and appreciative audience.

It would be interesting to look back into the past and to follow the history of this intersexual rivalry with all its ups and downs, its interludes of comparative peace and its sharp periods of active war. The position of women in society at any particular moment of history has a very strong influence on the subjects with which we are concerned in love, marriage and family, and we are apt to forget how great have been the changes in the status of women during the last two centuries. The following quotations taken from Dr. Violet Klein's book *The Feminine Character* illustrate this change very well. The first quotation takes the form of an extract from *The Times* of

22 July, 1797. "The increasing value of the fair sex is regarded by many writers as the certain index of a growing civilization. Smithfield (a market well known for its sales of women!) may for this reason claim to be a contributor to the particular progress of finesse, for in the market the price was again raised from one half a guinea to three and a half."

In order to convince readers who might be inclined to scout this idea that women could actually be purchased in such an enlightened country as England less than two centuries ago, another quotation on the same subject will be added. It is taken from *Woman's Coming of Age*, edited by S. M. Schmalhauser and Y. Calverton (Liveright, New York, 1931). It refers to a court case in 1814 and puts on record that a certain "Henry Cook of Effingham, Surrey, was forced under the bastardy laws to marry a woman of Slinfold, Sussex, and six months after the marriage she and her child were removed to the Effingham Workhouse. The governor there, having contracted to maintain all the poor for the specific sum of £210, complained of the new arrivals, whereupon the parish officer *prevailed on Cook to sell his wife*. The master of the workhouse, Chippen, was directed to take the woman to Croydon market and there on 17 June 1815 she was sold to John Earl for the sum of one shilling, which had been given to Earl for the purchase. To bind the bargain the following receipt was made out:

5/- stamp   June 17, 1815
Received of John Earl the sum of one shilling, in full
for my lawful wife by me HENRY COOK
Daniel Cook —
John Chippen *Witnesses*

In their satisfaction of having got rid of the chargeability of the woman the parish officers of Effingham paid the expenses of the journey to Croydon, including refreshments there, and also allowed a leg of mutton for the wedding dinner which took place in Earl's parish of Dorking.

These astonishing sales of women in England continued well into the nineteenth century and Ralph Waldo Emerson comments on them as follows in his book, *English Traits*, published in the year 1856. "The right of the husband to sell his wife has been retained down to our time."

This was the status of women of the lower classes in Great Britain in the middle of the nineteenth century and that the standing of women across the Channel was still lower can be gathered from the fact that on the Continent England was often referred to as the "Wives' Paradise". In 1725, Daniel Defoe wrote that if a cross-channel bridge were to be built all continental women would have made use of it to get to England. The nineteenth century witnessed the beginning of the Industrial Age and millions of women were employed in the less skilled and less well paid factory jobs. The same century saw also the rise of the middle classes and a growing veneration for wealth and all that this entailed.

As Miss Klein has written in her book *The Feminine Character* the prosperity brought about by industry produced in the new upper and middle classes an ambition to compete with each other in the outward signs of this prosperity. They vied therefore with each other in their spending, in their finery and in the idleness of their women. The men of these classes scouted the idea that their wives or their daughters would ever need to engage in any profitable work and if by any mishap their womenfolk were eventually forced to earn a living, the only two careers open to them were those of the governess and the needlewoman.

But at a later date there arose work of an unpaid kind with which middle and upper class women were allowed to occupy themselves. The contrast between the living conditions of the factory workers and of the upper two classes became so great that it awoke a growing concern among the more thoughtful upper-class women about the state of their poorer sisters. The history of social reform in the nineteenth century is full of the names of upper and middle-class women who were pioneers in one field or another of social endeavour; Hannah Martineau, the most distinguished publicist and political leader-writer of her time; Octavia Hill, a founder of the Charity Organization Society; Elizabeth Fry, the prison reformer; Florence Nightingale of Crimea war fame, Baroness Burdett-Coutts and Josephine Butler, were among them. All these exceedingly capable women helped to create a new feminine type, entirely different from that, which had been, up till then, socially acceptable.

From this bridgehead of women interested in social problems longing looks were cast on other fields of feminine endeavour, such as the fields of politics, business and science. A "Woman's Cause" was thereby created and by fighting and winning such outposts as reform of the marriage laws, enfranchisement, equal citizenship and better education, a vanguard of gallant feminists penetrated into the outer defences of the man-made world. But the opposition to feminist claims was both strong and bitter, not only amongst men, but also amongst women.

So great did the noise become that it eventually disturbed Queen Victoria resting at Osborne House in the Isle of Wight. She issued a royal appeal to all women of good will to "join in checking this mad wicked folly of Woman's Rights with all its attendant horrors on which my feeble sex is bent, forgetting every sense of womanly feeling and propriety. God created man and woman differently, then let them remain each in their own position. Woman would become the most hateful, heartless and disgusting of human beings were she allowed to unsex herself, and where would be the protection which man was intended to give the weaker sex?" So wrote the royal representative of the so-called feebler sex, the great Queen, who through-out her long life never, if she could help it, committed herself to the protection of anybody, whether male or female. But the feminist advance could not be arrested and within twenty years of Queen Victoria's death women attained almost all that they had fought for.

All this has had a very marked effect on the attitude of women to marriage. It has also produced greater difficulties for men. It was one thing to be married to an adoring and obedient young wife of the nineteenth century and another thing to be married to a sophisticated independent young woman, more highly educated than her husband.

Women have always been enigmas to men and any man who imagines that he can read them is a fool. "When I say that I know woman" wrote the great novelist Thackeray—and it is the business of novelists to study women—"I mean that I *don't* know them. Every single woman I ever knew is a puzzle to me, as I have no doubt she is to herself."

Freud was of the same opinion about women and like Thackeray regarded them as unpredictable and beyond the male's comprehension. "Throughout the ages the problem of woman has puzzled people of every kind", he wrote, and then added as an afterthought; "It is not to be expected that women will have pondered the question for they are themselves the riddle."

John Donne, poet and Dean of St. Paul's, strikes a similar note when he writes about women. *Defence of Women's Inconstancy*—"Learning affords no rules to know, much less knowledge to rule, the mind of a Woman. . . . Every woman is a Science; for he that plods upon a woman all his life long, shall at length finde himself short of knowledge of her; they are born to take down pride of wit, and ambition of wisdom, making *fools* wise in the adventuring to win them, wise men fools in conceit of losing their labours; *witty* men stark mad, being confounded with their uncertainties. . . . *Philosophers* write against them for spight, not desert, that having attained to some knowledge in all other things, in them only they know nothing, but are merely ignorant. . . . Now who can deny, but such as are obstinately bent to undervalue their worth, are those that have not soul enough to comprehend their excellency, Women being the most excellent creatures, in that Man is able to subject all things else, and to grow wise in everything but still persists a fool in Woman? The great *Scholler* if he once take a wife, is found so unlearned that he must begin his *Horn-book*, and all is by 'Inconstancy'. To conclude therefore; this name of *Inconstancy* which hath so much been poysoned with slander, ought to be changed into *variety*, for the which the world is so delightfull, and a Woman for that the most delightful thing in this world."

What are these unreadable and unpredictable features in women which have bewildered men ever since the beginning of time? Why are women so much more perplexing to men than men are to women? Is it because men are by nature much less complicated, more direct and more open than women are, or is it because women are so much more discerning in reading character than men? These are difficult questions to answer, but because there are psychological differences between the sexes and because these differences often occasion difficulties in marriage, it is a subject which is of present interest to us.

Many people have written on this subject but I know of no one who has done so with greater fairness and understanding than Sir Adolphe Abrahams in his little book *Woman: Man's Equal.* He starts with characteristic diplomacy by choosing a title for his book which leaves us in doubt, even after we have read it, as to whether women are or are not equal to men, and then shelves the whole riddle for good by remarking that men and women are *complementary*. This being so such words as inferiority and superiority are quite irrelevant to any discussion of the subject.

"Woman", he writes, "has a unique function in bearing and feeding a child, a function that necessarily handicaps her in competition with man, free from this obligation and its physical consequences. She may feel entitled to claim this function as evidence of superiority." Sir Adolphe is right in putting woman's responsibility for the continuation of the race in the forefront of any account of her psychological characteristics for it is her work as a mother which explains her peculiarities. Oswald Schwarz attributes the difficulty of predicting a woman's behaviour to the fact that whereas man revolves round the single centre of his brain woman describes an ellipse around the twin centres of her womb and her brain. And it is quite true that however intellectual and sophisticated a woman may be, however little she may seem to be interested in children and however difficult it may be for us to visualize her as a mother, the child-bearing factor exerts a constant effect on her behaviour.

Biologically speaking therefore woman must be considered superior to man in that she is the sustainer of the race and in order to render her fitter for her duties Nature has made her by far the tougher of the two sexes. More female infants survive than male infants, a woman's expectation of life is longer by three and a half years than that of a man and she is less susceptible than he is to malignant growths. She suffers less from heart disease than a man does and she is also exempt from a number of illnesses to which the male is prone. She is inferior only in muscular strength, but it is astonishing what she can manage to do with her slighter musculature. In more primitive countries it is the woman and not the man who provides the bulk of the labour; it is the woman who shoulders the heavier burdens and who works for the longest hours in the fields. In short the peasant woman has gained a world wide reputation for toughness.

What other differences are there between men and women? Woman has always been regarded as being more passive and receptive and man as being more active and inventive and there is truth in this observation. It is also safe to assert that a woman is by nature more emotional than a man and less swayed by reason. So long as she remains within her own domain, for which she has been specially equipped, that of the house and the family, she reigns supreme, but whenever she ventures outside that domestic circle she is less likely to be successful. There are, of course, many exceptions to this rule but it is nevertheless true that it is man and not woman who has been responsible for all that is best in the fields of science, philosophy and the arts.

Sir Adolphe Abrahams declares that in a "statistical study of Eminent Women from the dawn of history to the present day less than a thousand have accomplished anything that history has recorded as worth while; and many of these had acquired fame and fortune by means other than intellectual brilliance." Only in two of the arts have women ever excelled, namely in the arts of acting and of dancing. It is noteworthy also that when women have managed to achieve a very high level of intellectual creative work it will generally be found that they have either worked in collaboration with a male or else have developed in their own characters some of the physical and psychological attributes of the male. Several of these masculine types of women have actually dressed and lived as much as possible as men at a time when it required much courage to do this. Madame Curie, Elizabeth Barrett Browning, George Eliot and Beatrice Webb are examples of women who did their best work in partnership with men and Rosa Bonheur, George Sand, Madame de Stael and Madame Blavatsky are examples of women who preferred to live and who affronted public opinion by living actually as men lived.

It may be objected that women have only comparatively recently been admitted into professions which were previously entirely closed to them and consequently that they have not yet had sufficient time to attain great eminence in them. But this is not strictly true for women have now been working as doctors and lawyers for at least a quarter of a century and yet no woman has yet attained pre-eminence in these professions. There have been and are of course many excellent female physicians, surgeons, solicitors and barristers but no woman doctor or lawyer has yet appeared who was or who is superior to the leading men of these professions.

Sir Adolphe Abrahams, formerly Dean of Westminster Hospital Medical School, is of the opinion that the same generalization can be made with regard to the attainments of schoolboys and schoolgirls and of men and women medical students. He writes: "Boys tend to spread into extremes of dullness or brightness, girls approximate to an average. Much the same applies to adolescents, as for example in the co-education in medical schools. The best girls are rarely as good as the best men, but their average ability is superior. They are more painstaking and bookish, show greater application and patience in routine work continuous at low pressure, but are less practical. They memorize better but are inferior in reasoning power and judgment." If female readers are disposed to regard the above statements that there have been few great women scientists, doctors or lawyers as derogatory to their sex, they can take comfort in the fact that there are fewer women at the lower end of the intellectual ladder amongst the feebleminded and the idiots. Congenital malformations are also commoner amongst boys, one of the few exceptions to this rule being malformations of the palate.

Most readers will agree with the statement often made that women are more interested in people and that men are more interested in ideas. For example a woman is more likely to be concerned with the characters described in a book and with her own reactions to them, whereas the man's attention will be directed more to the general situation described in the book and to the psychological principles which these characters serve to illustrate. The woman's view of the book will consequently be more subjective than that of the man. For this reason it has been said that no woman would be capable of acting as a judge; she would be too much concerned with the character of the prisoner and too little concerned with the fact that he had broken the law. But is this altogether a disadvantage that a judge should be very much preoccupied with the human element in the trial?

Most people agree that women are more adaptable than are men and also that they are better able to endure suffering and disaster. That they have a great capacity to adjust themselves to changes in their circumstances is shown by the readiness with which a girl acclimatizes herself to marriage with a man who was formerly above her in social station. So also is it true that the wife of a self-made man finds it much easier than her husband does to acquire the manners and usages of the higher social circles with which they are called upon to deal. Sir Adolphe Abrahams has no doubt at all of the woman's greater ability to endure pain and misfortune. He writes of this as follows: "Some conspicuous features of feminine superiority call for unqualified admiration. Woman's capacity for enduring suffering, facing disaster and misfortune or impending death is an everyday experience."

Much has been written about women's lack of logic and about their use of intuition in place of reasoning and it is quite true that men and women often arrive at decisions by entirely different paths. Women have a hearty distaste for all rigid rules of thought and the fact that the man's more pedestrian methods of reaching a conclusion are on the whole more reliable than their methods are, carries no weight with them. They much prefer to by-pass all analysis, all weighing of alternatives and all reasoning and to arrive at their answer directly by means of intuition. Now although the word intuition is often misused by the female sex in argument and although a woman will frequently use it as a cloak for stubborness and self-will, intuition is a faculty which nevertheless exists, a faculty which reaches truth directly and without any previous process of reasoning. This is a fact which males often refuse to accept.

There has now arisen a new school of thought which discounts all these supposed innate differences between masculine and feminine minds and which regards them, if they exist at all, as being conditioned and not inborn. It has to be remembered that from the very beginning of our lives the grown-ups around us have been busily engaged in conditioning us for social life. They have taught us that certain things should not be done if we are boys and that other things should not be done if we are girls and have thereby established in our minds very different codes of conduct. For example a boy must always maintain a stiff upper lip and must never display his real feelings to the world. He must also occupy his time in certain manly pursuits and must be indifferent, and perhaps a little contemptuous, of the quieter interests and occupations of girls. So also is a girl taught to be more modest and gentler than her brother and to behave as it is right and seemly that a girl should behave. Those who belong to this new school of thought point out that the lessons inculcated by these adults are quite artificial and that the said sexual differences are consequently non-existent. In other words the so-called sex differences are *acquired* and not *inherited*. The American anthropologist Margaret Meade has given very strong support to this school of thought by her anthropological researches in New Guinea. She described in her books, three primitive tribes living within a short distance of each other in New Guinea and states that in all three of these tribes the standards of male and female behaviour were entirely different. In the first tribe the behaviour of *both* the men and women could be described as maternal, womanly, passive and non-aggressive, in the second tribe the behaviour of *both* sexes was masculine, active, virile and aggressive and in the third tribe the rôles played by the man and the woman were the reverse of those to which we are accustomed. In this third tribe the women played a masculine rôle and the men a feminine rôle. For example the women assumed all the responsibility for the administration of tribal affairs and supplied the tribe's means of livelihood and thereby freed the men to follow what was regarded as being their true vocation, that of the creative artist. For every man in this third tribe was an artist and not in one art only, but "in dancing, carving, painting and so on".

What conclusions are we to draw from these different opinions concerning the distinctive psychological features of the two sexes. My own view is that Nature has made the psychological functioning of the two sexes complementary to each other and that in spite of what Margaret Meade asserts there exists an innate psychological difference between a man and a woman. I happen to subscribe to an Eastern system of psychology which asserts that individuals are divisible into two parts, Essence and Personality. A new born baby possesses only Essence and this includes characteristics, potentialities and traits which are awaiting development in him. Personality is what the baby subsequently acquires as the result of education and imitation of those around him and it sometimes happens that what he was born with and what he acquires are in conflict with each other.

Men and women are in essence different from each other but they may acquire characteristics which to some extent contradict and obliterate their inborn difference, so that the woman becomes aggressive and active and the man submissive and passive. It is in this way that I explain the strange anomalies found by Margaret Meade in her New Guinea researches. This accounts for the differences in the rôles played by the men and women in the three New Guinea tribes studied by her. It also accounts for some of the inner conflicts experienced by individual men and women who have been conditioned to behave in ways which are contradictory to their essence. There are, for example, essentially feminine women who have been conditioned to lead busy professional or business lives and to ape the ways of men, women who in the secret recesses of their hearts are longing to be wives and mothers. In essence men and women are not only different but also complementary to each other and if these essential differences cannot be expressed or are reversed, as when a woman becomes active and aggressive or a man passive and submissive, they are invariably unhappy. It is in this way that I explain not only the strange confusions described by Margaret Meade but also the cases of deep unhappiness met with in certain individual men and women.

12

FAMILY PLANNING

FEW couples deliberately elect to remain permanently childless but they use contraceptive methods for certain purposes, such as to postpone the arrival of the first child, to avoid too rapid an expansion of the family, and eventually to limit its size. So also are birth control societies anxious to stress the positive rather than the negative aspect of their work and for this reason they now call themselves by such names as Family Planning Associations, instead of by the older denomination of societies for the spread of knowledge of birth control methods. And it is quite understandable that they should lay emphasis on the constructive aspects of birth control, for more nonsense has been talked about the evils and dangers of contraception than about most subjects.

Birth control is no recent discovery, for it is mentioned both in the Old Testament and in the Ebers papyrus. Contraceptive methods have also been employed for many centuries by certain primitive tribes and peoples, the favoured method being the taking of some vegetable extract which arrests the process of ovulation. One of the best known of these sterilizing extracts is that made from Lithospermum, an extract which has recently been submitted to scientific tests. But in spite of birth control's antiquity widespread interest in it began in this country only towards the close of the last century; it is at that period of history that the following account of the birth control movement in Great Britain really starts.

In the year 1876 two people—a man and a woman—appeared before the Lord Chief Justice on the charge "that they were unlawfully and wickedly devising, contriving, and intending, as much as in them lay, to vitiate and corrupt the morals as well of youth as of divers other subjects of the Queen, and to incite and encourage the said subjects to indecent, obscene, unnatural and immoral practices and bring them to a state of wickedness, lawlessness and debauchery."

This indictment has been quoted at length because it is a landmark in the history of birth control in Great Britain. As travellers sometimes look back from some vantage point in their journey at the route along which they have travelled, so it is of interest now to take stock of the progress of the birth control movement in Great Britain, a movement which, owing to the rapid increase of the world's population, has now become of world-wide importance.

The crime of which Bradlaugh and Annie Besant were accused in 1876 was that they had delivered by hand a new edition of Knowlton's pamphlet on birth-control to the Chief Clerk at Guildhall and had informed that official that they would be returning next day to sell this same work to the general public.

This was a challenge which the law was forced to take up and it promptly did so. Its ponderous machinery went into action and a verdict of guilty was returned by a jury against the two offenders. They appealed against this verdict and fortunately won their case. So ridiculous does the wording of this indictment seem to us now, that we are surprised that it was drawn up by solemn-faced lawyers of only seventy years ago. The law is said to lag a hundred years behind public opinion but the fact that it was a jury which brought in the verdict of guilty shows that the public at that time looked upon birth control with the same aversion as the law.

"The heterodoxies of one generation became the orthodoxies

of the next" and this is certainly true of public opinion on the subject of birth control. Few voices are now raised against it, and even the Anglican Church has come to see that there are occasions on which the use of contraceptive measures is justifiable. But the Church of Rome still maintains its former rock-like attitude to contraception, and in his Encyclical Letter of 1930 Pope Pius XI restated its views on this subject. "The conjugal act is of its very nature designed for the procreation of offspring; and therefore those who in performing it deliberately deprive it of its natural power and efficacy, act against nature and do something which is shameful and intrinsically immoral." The Anglican Church has gone back on its original decision mainly for two reasons. First, it was aware of the fact that intelligent lay opinion as well as the opinion of many of its own bishops was in favour of family planning, and second, that there often existed excellent medical reasons why a woman should avoid conception. The Lambeth Conference of 1930 therefore gave members of the Anglican Church a great deal of freedom of action in this matter. It agreed that "where there was a clearly felt moral obligation to limit or to avoid parenthood, and where there was a morally sound reason for avoiding complete abstinence, other methods might be used."

The only method of birth control sanctioned by the Roman Church is the method which takes advantage of what has become known as the "safe period", that is to say, those days in the woman's menstrual cycle when she is least likely to conceive. In his first Encyclical the Pope made a rather vague pronouncement on this subject which was not sufficiently explicit to permit of anybody being certain as to what he meant, but in his address to midwives in 1951 he was much more definite and spoke of the "safe period" in the menstrual cycle. There are reasons for believing that this more direct reference of his to the so-called "safe period" method was a concession to the many younger members of the Catholic Church who were and still are finding it difficult to obey the Church's hard ruling on birth control. This is not surprising, for up till that time the only means by which they could avoid increasing the size of their families was to remain chaste and to be married and to remain chaste was asking of them more than any Church has the right to expect.

For a young couple in love with each other and sharing the intimacies of the home to remain continent indefinitely is well-nigh impossible. Those who feel that this is an exaggeration, and that with determination young married people can live together as brothers and sisters, would profit by reading the statement made by Palladius on the experiences of the early Christians. He wrote: "These men were vigorous and resolute. They were whole-heartedly devoted to the ideal of asceticism, they were living under the best possible conditions for cultivating such ideals, and their régime was austere to a degree that is for us impossible. Yet there was nothing that troubled them as much as sexual temptation, and this trouble to some degree persisted throughout life". (Quoted by Havelock Ellis).

If men who have sacrificed everything for the sake of their religious ideals, who have accepted an austere form of life gladly, and who are living under conditions ideal to the maintenance of chastity, find such difficulties in repressing their sexuality, how can young married men and women in love with each other be expected to do it. The only couples likely to attain the standard of control demanded of them by the Roman Church are those who have never obtained any real sexual satisfaction, or couples who are not really in love with each other. The price that an enforced chastity exacts of a young Catholic couple in love with each other is well illustrated by the following case-sheet taken from my own files.

Mr. X. is a young Irish labourer who already has a family of seven children, although he is only thirty-two years of age and his wife only twenty-eight. Not being able to afford any more, and finding it quite impossible to live with his wife as brother and sister, Mr. X has left Ireland and has come to England where wages are higher. It being impossible for him to purchase contraceptive articles in Ireland he is now seeking sterilization in order that he may be able to return to his wife and his family, to whom he is obviously devoted.

It is, however, the world situation which provides the most weighty arguments in favour of birth control. The great fall in the death rate, and particularly in the infant mortality rate, has led to so rapid an increase in population in many parts of the world that shortage of food is becoming a more and more serious problem. It is no exaggeration to say that unless something is done to reduce the rate of this rapid increase of the world's population, a serious situation is likely to arise within the next fifty years. The populations of Japan and of India are now so rapidly outstripping available food supplies that the national authorities are becoming thoroughly alarmed about it and are giving every encouragement to the spread of information on the subject of contraceptive measures. Because the results of this crusade in favour of birth control in Japan have been insufficient as yet to bring about any appreciable diminution in the rate of increase, the Japanese are being compelled to make use of the highly undesirable method of legalized abortion. A very large percentage of pregnancies in that country now end in that way.

But it is with birth control on the individual rather than on the national scale that we are here concerned, and one of the first general statements that can be made on this subject is that no harm is likely to result from the use of an approved method of contraception. This statement is necessary if for no other reason than that some Catholic doctors have attempted to find medical reasons for supporting the ordinance of the Roman Catholic Church by suggesting that birth control is injurious to the user. In the opinion of the great majority of their medical colleagues, the methods recommended by the various birth control and family planning societies are quite harmless to health.

One of the objections brought against contraceptive measures by Catholic doctors is that they tend to lower fertility, so that after they have been left off the couple may be unable to have the child whose arrival they had only intended to postpone. This statement contains a small element of truth, for contraceptive measures mask any infertility which happens to exist in the wife or in the husband, with the result that it is only found out when they have been discontinued. Valuable time in which treatment might have been instituted is thereby lost. If the wife is no longer in the twenties but, say, in the later thirties, this time factor may be of very great importance, for the fertility of a woman drops during the thirties and still more steeply in the forties. The factor of the wife's age should therefore always be kept in mind when deciding to postpone the arrival of the first child.

Birth control can be used for a number of different purposes: (1) for arranging that pregnancy should occur at the best time for both mother and child; (2) for avoiding a pregnancy which might be injurious to the mother's health; (3) to prevent the birth of a child which ran a serious risk of inheriting some family disease; (4) to keep the size of the family within the limits imposed by the family purse. Statistics can be quoted which show the need for spacing births and for preventing pregnancies from following each other too rapidly. They show that first babies die slightly more frequently than second babies do, and that after the birth of the second child there occurs a steady rise in the infantile mortality rate. By the time that the seventh child has been born the mortality rate is fifty per cent. higher than it was for the first baby, and after the birth of the tenth child it is two hundred per cent. higher. What is of even greater importance than this rise in child mortality is the strain which too rapid child-bearing imposes on the mother. Now the death of an infant is to be deplored, but the death of a mother, and perhaps the mother of a large family, is a far greater tragedy.

It has to be accepted that the ideal method of birth control has yet to be discovered and that all of the methods in general use suffer from some disadvantage. To be considered ideal a contraceptive measure should have the following attributes: it should be entirely reliable and have no effect other than that of preventing conception; it should be simple, cheap and fool-proof, and it should offend as little as possible the social, religious and aesthetic feelings of the user. All methods at present in use fail in one way or another to come up to this ideal. As will later be seen, the great majority of them act by introducing either a mechanical or a chemical obstacle to the passage of spermatozoa into the womb, and such methods can be sub-divided into two main groups, those used by the male, and those for which the female makes herself responsible.

But before the various techniques of contraception are des-cribed, something must be said about obtaining expert advice on this subject. If the family doctor is consulted as a first step, he will either deal with the matter himself, or else he will refer the wife to a gynaecologist or a gynaecological clinic. But here she may run up against unexpected difficulties, unless the practi-tioner has been very careful in his choice. There are many gynaecologists and gynaecological hospital clinics which show no interest at all in contraceptive measures and dislike being bothered with enquiries on the subject. Many women patients have reported that although they have been warned at a hos-pital clinic that it would be very unwise for them to become pregnant again, no advice is given them as to how this catastrophe can be avoided. "The doctor said to my husband that if I became pregnant again I should probably lose my, life, but he didn't tell me or my husband what to do about it". Such a remark as this is by no means uncommon. So also are women frequently discharged from our leading hospitals with warnings of this kind, but without any advice having been given on the subject of contraception.

Fortunately, there have now been established throughout the country special clinics at which the best advice can be obtained. The Family Planning Association has close on two hundred centres, which handle as many as fifty thousand new cases annually. Other centres of this kind bear the name of that great pioneer in the birth-control movement, Dr. Marie Stopes. These clinics fill what would otherwise have been a bad gap in our health services, by giving advice not only on birth control but also on the allied subject of fertility.

The first contraceptive methods to be studied are those which require no equipment at all but only cleverness on the part of the husband or the wife. The most important of these two methods is that of withdrawing the male organ just prior to ejaculation, and that this method is highly popular has been confirmed by questioning a hundred consecutive patients at the Ealing Birth Control Clinic. When these hundred women were asked what methods they had previously employed, they replied as follows:

Withdrawal	57 patients
Use of a sheath	33 ,,
Chemical pessaries	9 ,,
Post-coital douches	9 ,,
Total abstention	5 ,,

The great advantage of withdrawal is that it requires no apparatus and no preparation before intercourse. Its chief disadvantages are that it requires very careful timing, and that as mistakes can easily be made in this the method cannot be considered entirely reliable. It has also been held to be responsible for the development of anxiety states in the husband and of sexual dissatisfaction on the part of the wife. Now it is quite true that withdrawal or *coitus interruptus*, as it is often called, diminishes the wife's chances of obtaining full satisfaction if the husband is able to maintain intercourse for only a short time, but if he has acquired the capacity to maintain intercourse for longer, there can be no objection at all to withdrawal from the point of view of his wife. I am also of the opinion that far too much has been made of the bad effects of withdrawal on the husband. Anxiety can be associated with the use of all the contraceptive methods, more especially if they have failed on some previous occasion, and I see no reasons for regarding withdrawal as particularly liable to produce anxiety conditions. It is, of course, obvious that this method is not suited to nervous or unskilful husbands but only to those who have attained a certain proficiency in coital control. It must, however, be conceded that withdrawal is not a hundred per cent. certain, and for this reason it is generally advisable to reduce the small risk of failure by supplementing withdrawal with some additional contraceptive measure, such as the insertion into the vagina of a spermicidal pessary after intercourse has been completed.

The only other method of birth control which requires no apparatus is that which is countenanced by the Catholic Church, namely, the use of the so-called "safe period". This method is based on the fact that a woman can only conceive if intercourse has taken place at or near the time at which the egg-cell is liberated from the ovary and descends into the womb. This period of fertility in the woman is very brief and lasts from three days before to one day after ovulation has occurred, that is to say, it is restricted to only four days of the menstrual cycle.

In order to make u e of this method a very careful record of periods must previously have been kept for at least six months, for the purpose of finding out how regular the woman's periods are. The four days of fertility can then be found out by calculating that the ovum will be liberated fourteen days *before* the onset of the *next* period, and it is this necessity for counting *back* from a *future* event which makes the safe period method a difficult one to use. If all menstrual cycles were of the same length, then the calculation would be comparatively simple, but even amongst women who regard themselves as "regular", a discrepancy of two or three days is by no means uncommon. It is for this reason that the preliminary six months' record of cycles is required. With its help the wife will be able to estimate with greater accuracy which day the fourteenth day before her next period is likely to be. Having fixed this day, she can then regard four days before this date and one day after it as her "fertile" period. Intercourse will then be permissible any time *outside* this restriction period.

Two additional observations can be made use of in order to confirm the accuracy of the calculated date of ovulation. If the temperature be carefully charted first thing every morning, the day of ovulation will be signalled by a slight but abrupt rise in the morning temperature. The other confirmatory sign is the occasional occurrence of abdominal pain and of slight vaginal bleeding (*Mittelschmerz*) on the day of ovulation.

The success of this method depends entirely on the care and intelligence of the user and on the regularity of her periods. It becomes less and less reliable as menstruation becomes less regular on account of such disturbing factors as upsets in health and emotional crises. Although the use of the method has been associated with so many failures in this country that a facetious writer on the subject once remarked that a whole family could be acquired in determining which *was* the safe period, the

Margaret Sanger Bureau in New York is now using it with considerable success. It would be interesting to know whether any Catholic statistics on this subject are yet available.

From the Ealing statistics it will be seen that the next most popular method in this country is the use of a rubber sheath or condon. This method may fail, and the commonest cause of failure is breakage, but as the quality of sheaths improves, breakage is becoming rarer and rarer. The three main objections to the use of a sheath is first that it entails an artificial and highly undesirable interruption of the love-making in order to apply the sheath, that it reduces the sensation for the male, and that it necessitates the use of artificial lubricants. But what is of greater importance than any of these objections is the fact that weakly sexed husbands find the wearing of a sheath so difficult that they meet with frequent failures in intercourse. The sexual act is so precariously balanced for some husbands that anything of an inhibiting nature is liable to upset it, and it is not surprising, therefore, that the need to stop and adjust such an artificial encumbrance as a sheath is quite sufficient to bring about a failure.

The rubber sheath is a measure suited only to special circumstances, such as the following: at the beginning of married life, when the wife has not yet been fitted with an occlusive pessary; after childbirth before the occlusive pessary has been refitted; in those exceptional circumstances in which for anatomical or other reasons an occlusive cap or pessary cannot be used, or in which the wife has a strong revulsion against using any such contrivance. It should also be borne in mind that the vendors of rubber goods are not always honest, and that they sometimes take advantage of their customer's ignorance to charge him very high prices for goods which are said to be of exceptionally high quality.

The other methods in common use are those for which the wife is responsible, and they include douching, the use of contraceptive jellies and chemical pessaries, and the wearing of such mechanical devices as the Dutch cap and the Cervical cap. The oldest and cheapest of all these methods is douching, but its chief defect is that it is useless unless the douching is very efficiently done, so that the injected fluid distends the walls of the vagina and opens up all its folds. Because of this defect, douching is now only used as a supplementary measure, and the same can also be said of such contraceptive measures as spermicidal jellies, chemical suppositories and pastes. All of these methods are excellent when they are used in conjunction with some mechanical device which prevents the semen from reaching the cervix. The adoption of two separate lines of defence, the one mechanical and the other chemical, greatly increases the efficiency of birth control.

Three types of cap are in common use in this country, known as the Dutch, the Dumas, and the Cervical varieties respectively, and the principle underlying their use is the same. All of these caps are rubber diaphragms with stiffened edges which, when they are placed correctly within the vagina, prevent the semen from reaching the region of the cervical canal. The efficiency of the various caps is markedly increased by lubricating them before insertion with spermicidal pastes and jellies, which have the effect of rendering the spermatozoa motionless. To obtain still greater security a chemical suppository may also be inserted *after* intercourse has taken place.

It is essential that the cap should be properly fitted by a doctor who at the same time shows the patient how to insert it and to remove it herself. The ease and celerity with which this is learnt varies greatly with different patients, and also with the skill and experience of the instructor. As there are very few instances in which this excellent form of birth control cannot be used, it should be the method of choice unless there exists some special reason for not making use of it. Some women start with a dislike of the idea of introducing into themselves any mechanical appliance, but this initial prejudice is soon overcome in the great majority of cases. Only a few women are so stubborn or so prejudiced as to refuse to make even a trial of it.

But as has been pointed out, the ideal method of control has not yet been discovered, all present-day methods having one or another disadvantage attached to them. On theoretical grounds the most promising method would be to interfere with the process of fertilization by entirely preventing the formation of spermatozoa in the male, or by arresting the liberation of ova in the female. Experiments are being made along both these lines, but so far only with partial success. Unfortunately, only very limited funds are at present available for research on the subject of contraception. It is a type of investigation which makes very little appeal to those who contribute so generously to other lines of medical research, such as the search for a cure for cancer, yet if the truth is to be known, the need for a cheap, easy, foolproof, entirely reliable and safe method of birth control is far more pressing at the present time in humanity's history than the need for the discovery of a cure for cancer. Whilst the latter would aggravate the world problem of our overrunning our available food supply, the former would help to solve it.

It has been objected that if an ideal method of birth control were to be discovered it would promptly be abused and there is no doubt that it would be so. There is no human discovery which has not been put to wrong purposes, but surely this is no reason why all technical research should be abandoned. So also has it been said that the discovery of an easy and entirely reliable form of contraception would encourage an even greater sexual laxity than already exists. A similar objection was formerly brought against instruction in the use of prophylactic measures against infection by venereal diseases. It was said that if it became generally known that there were methods of protection against venereal peril, few young people would remain virtuous. What a terrible commentary on this age was this suggestion, that our virtues can survive only if we surround wrong-doing with palisades of fear. And if this statement were true would a virtue which was only the product of fear be worth preserving? No, fear is a poor counsellor whether it be the fear which masquerades in the individual as chastity or the fear which attends the meetings of the United Nations.

Birth control by surgical sterilization of the husband or wife has not yet been considered. Some people have dismissed this method as entirely unjustifiable on the grounds that it brings about a permanent sterility. Yet it undoubtedly has a place in family planning. It is true that the Nazi Government brought surgical sterilization into disrepute but totalitarian governments have brought many useful procedures into disrepute and their abuse of sterilization constitutes no real argument against its voluntary use. In the Scandinavian countries it has been legalised now for several years so that it can be carried out under certain safeguards. In this country the legal implications of these operations are uncertain, but in spite of this doubt such operations are being performed by doctors who are satisfied that they are necessary on certain occasions and medically justifiable.

Because sterilization of the male is a minor operation which can be carried out under a local anaesthetic, whilst sterilization of the female entails opening the abdomen, operation on the male is preferable to operation on the female, unless the woman's abdomen has to be opened for some other purpose. The chief medical vindication for surgical sterilization of the husband is in order to avoid conception in cases in which pregnancy would entail very grave danger to the wife or in which the family history is such that a child would run a serious risk of being born with some inheritable disease or malformation. It may be objected that conception can be avoided by the use of methods which do not bring about a state of permanent sterility but, as we have seen in this chapter, no contraceptive measure is at present a hundred per cent. certain.

I have come across many cases where husbands and wives have both been brought to such a pitch of anxiety by previous failures in contraception that any love-making between them has ceased. This is a highly undesirable state of affairs and one which may throw a great strain on the marriage. This being so, in such cases as these, sterilization of the husband will always have to be considered. It has been said that sterilization of the male by division of the ducts leading from the testicles brings about a permanent sterility but this is not necessarily true for it is perfectly feasible to re-unite the ducts by a subsequent operation. Although no surgeon could guarantee a successful result to this re-uniting operation there is a reasonable chance of its succeeding. In my opinion, voluntary sterilization by surgical operation is often justifiable.

Finally there is a crude method of family planning which is the outcome of despair and which is also a measure of the degree of failure attending other methods of birth control. It has been said, but I know not on what grounds, that from three to four hundred abortions are carried out in this country every day. An Interdepartmental Committee which investigated this subject in 1939 reported that between 110,000 and 150,000 miscarriages were artificially produced during the course of the four years 1935 to 1938 inclusive. And if records can be obtained of so large a number of abortions as this the number done in secret and without there being any records of them must be at least four times greater.

It is indeed quite impossible to estimate with any degree of accuracy the annual toll in abortions or to arrive at the amount of ill-health to women for which the abortion racket is responsible. Dr. Eustace Chesser states that at least twenty percent. of all pregnancies end in this way, and it is certainly true that, "the overwhelming majority of married women who have been married for five years or more have at some time or other sought, whether successfully or not, to end pregnancy". A few have succeeded in terminating it by their own unaided efforts by dint of taking violent exercise, by swallowing equally violent purgatives, or else by obtaining from the chemist a reliable "remedy for pregnancy"; But the majority of women with un- wanted pregnancies have had to make enquiry of friends or of people who should know, in order to obtain the addresses of "experts" who would be willing to help them.

In this way there have been established both a big industry in female pills and other remedies for pregnancy and an unofficial band of more or less expert professional abortionists. Now it is quite true that it is possible to get a pregnancy terminated legally by a reliable gynæcologist and in a hospital, provided that childbirth would endanger the mother's physical health but there may be other good reasons why a pregnancy should be brought to an end. A young and ignorant girl may have been seduced by some clever sexual adventurer or there may exist very strong psychological grounds why a pregnancy should not be allowed to go to full term.

But at present a woman who is determined to get rid of an unwanted pregnancy has no alternative to that of putting her- self blindly into the hands of a member of the underground army of abortionists, who by means of anything from skewers to electrical contrivances will endeavour to do what is required. There are good reasons also for believing that the number of these abortion specialists is steadily increasing and that more and more ill-health is being brought about by them. And who shall say that such specialists are not sometimes needed for the lack of anything better? If an enquiry were to be made of all medical men many would reply that on at least one occasion they had been tempted to aid a desperate woman for other reasons than danger to her physical health, but that they had refused because they could not afford to take the risk which it entailed.

What is required is first an improvement in contraceptive technique, so that failures become less frequent and second, an alteration in the law which should recognize wider grounds for legal abortion than the existence of damage to the mother's physical health. Eustace Chesser suggested that the following cases should be regarded as justifying legal abortion; girls who have become pregnant under the age of consent, girls who have been raped, pregnancies occurring in mentally deficient women or in women who are suffering from transmittable disease and finally pregnancies which are the result of incest. (Eustace Chesser, *Love without Fear* (Rich & Cowan, Medical Publications).

13

THE NEED FOR CHILDREN

IT was said in the previous chapter that few people marry with the avowed purpose of never having any children; when they use contraceptive methods they do so in order to limit the size of the family, to postpone the arrival of the first child, and to ensure a satisfactory spacing of the births. It is absurd, therefore, to accuse the present generation of selfishness and of preoccupation with their own personal comfort, as some writers have done, because they refuse to have as many children as their grandparents did.

There is an excellent reason for this refusal of theirs, namely, the fact that the parents of today are far more heavily penalized than were parents of an earlier age. In the past a family was regarded as being an economic asset, so that an agricultural labourer and his wife looked upon their growing family in the same way that a financier looks upon capital accumulating in his bank. They felt that these children would soon begin to earn money and to help with the household expenses. They also realized that the day would eventually arrive when these same children might be their sole comfort and support in their old age. No modern parents are able to regard their children in this light, for however much happiness they may bring into the home they can scarcely be looked upon as being a sound economic investment. Housing shortage, the impossibility of obtaining any domestic help in the home, the rise in the cost of living, and a great many other factors besides, have converted what was formerly a financial advantage into a serious financial loss.

Yet in spite of the hardships that this will entail, the great majority of couples want to have children, and it is fortunate that they should want them, for although marriage was instituted for the sake of the children, the children also support and strengthen the marriage. There can be no doubt that the triad of mother, father and child is a far more stable grouping than the duality of wife and husband, and this is a truth of which most couples are aware, even if they have not actually spoken of it.

The need for a third party in the home begins to be felt at a variable time after the marriage, and if no baby arrives then a dog or a cat is almost always imported as a substitute for it. What makes the significance of the newcomer so obvious is that the animal is treated and talked about in the same way as a child would be treated and talked about, for the "I" and the "you" with which the marriage started are no longer enough, and the "he" and the "she" have to be added to it. But the dog and the cat are not real substitutes for the child, and sooner or later the couple realize this fact. The matter is then discussed and agreement is usually reached.

If there be a difference of opinion it is more likely to be the husband who opposes the idea of children and for various reasons, valid and otherwise, such as the expense of it all, the upset it will cause in the home or the lack of suitable accommodation for children. These are the arguments he will flourish, but deep down in his subconscious mind there may also be a state of alarm at the prospect of a rival for his wife's affection. Should it be the wife who objects to the idea of a family, it will be for such reasons as that it will entail the abandonment of her business or professional career, that it will mean giving up certain conveniences and pleasures, that she is scared of the dangers of childbirth, or that she is unwilling to run the risk of losing her figure and of suddenly looking much older.

But if there are risks attached to having a family, there are also risks attached to *not* having a family and particularly the risk that without the help of children the marriage will eventually come to grief. A marriage can make an excellent start as a love and mutual benefit society for two, but unless the size of the said society is increased, the home will become little more than a convenient hotel for two entirely self-centred people. Children are a nuisance but they are an excellent antidote to the growth of egoism and also the source of a great deal of happiness and fun. To try to get on without them entails big risks.

All married people do not have a choice in this matter. According to the figures of the 1911 Census, 16·6 per cent of the married couples living in Great Britain are childless, and the corresponding figures for South Africa and Australia are 15 per cent. and 15·4 per cent respectively. Unfortunately, we have no reliable means of analysing these figures and of finding out how often their childlessness is voluntary and the result of the use of contraceptives, and how often it is involuntary and due to their infertility; but in the opinion of most authorities, about ten per cent of all marriages in this country are childless against the wishes of the couples concerned. This percentage agrees with the figures which were obtained by the Swedish authority on this subject, Dr. Alva Myrdal, who is of the opinion that ten per cent. of all Swedish marriages are childless involuntarily, that 7·5 per cent of couples are only able to have one child, and five per cent have two children but would have preferred more had they been able to have more. In other words, there are good reasons for believing that involuntary sterility plays quite an important rôle in the fall of the birth rates of some of the leading European countries. The practical lesson to be derived from these figures is that the fertility of the

should be reassured that the request for an examination does not indicate that their manhood is being called into question, but that it is being asked for because infertility factors are sometimes found on both sides. And this statement has the advantage of being true. In a very large number of cases the causes of the childlessness are multiple.

The examination of the husband is a simple one and can be divided into three parts: (1) an enquiry into the efficiency and the frequency of intercourse; (2) an investigation of the husband's past medical history and of his present state of health; (3) a complete analysis of his semen. Semen analysis has now become so complicated that it has to be done in a properly equipped laboratory and by a worker accustomed to such investigations. Amongst the things which have to be known are the number of spermatozoa present in a given quantity of semen, their mobility, the length of time they remain "alive" at room temperature, their uniformity and their appearance. The specimens to be examined have to be fresh and preferably not more than two or three hours old. The best method of obtaining them is by practising withdrawal or *coitus interruptus*.

The examination of the wife is usually more elaborate and should include a general gynæcological examination of the reproductive system and a special investigation of the patency of the Fallopian tubes through which the ova have to pass on their way to the uterus. These structures are tested either by insoufflation, that is to say, by blowing air through them or else by taking X-ray pictures after they have been filled with some opaque substance. Another useful test is the so-called postcoital test, that is to say, the microscopic investigation of a drop of fluid taken from the entrance to the womb some hours after intercourse. This will show whether or not spermatozoa are managing to penetrate into the womb.

Two more things should be realized, the first that the fertility of men and women can change from time to time, either for the better or the worse, so that it must not be taken for granted that a wife who has borne a child, say, three years ago, is capable of bearing a child now. Both her own and her husband's fertility may have changed during these three years, so that it is advisable to reassess it. The second point to bear in mind is that grave infertility is quite compatible with the possession of perfect health. This truth has to be emphasized because it is quite common for a patient to say: "I did not bother to get myself examined because I felt so well that I did not think it possible that anything could be wrong with me."

Sometimes the infertility or sterility is incurable, so that all hope of having a child has to be abandoned. Should this happen the childless couple may decide to adopt a child, and the results obtained from this measure are usually admirable. It is surprising how quickly the foster-parents seem to forget that the child is not actually their own and what pleasure they obtain from lavishing on the child a surcharge of parental affection. Too much has been made of the difficulties which will have to be faced when the child is later told the truth about his or her parentage. There has been much discussion about the age at which the news should be imparted and by whom, and it is satisfactory to know that adoption societies now discourage the child being told anything at all, unless there be special reasons for its knowing the truth. What purpose will be served by the child knowing it? This is a question which foster-parents should ponder over very carefully before they do anything at all.

Every now and then the completely unexpected miracle happens after a child has been adopted. Anxiety may have an adverse effect on the reproductive systems both of a man and of a woman, and the repeated disappointments the wife has previously undergone are quite likely to have lowered her fertility.

After she has accepted her fate and all treatment has ceased, her anxiety disappears and the unexpected thing occasionally happens—she conceives.

It was said that when sterility cannot be cured there is only one remedy left, namely the adoption of a child, but this is true only of sterility on the part of the wife. If it be the husband who is at fault, then there exists a possible alternative to adopting a child, namely, that the wife should be inseminated with fertile semen from another source. This question of artificial insemination is sufficiently important to make it necessary to discuss it more fully.

The point I wish to make clear is that it is for the couple alone to decide whether or not they will have recourse to this remedy. They can, of course, talk the matter over with their doctor, but since ethical principles are involved in insemination with donated semen, the final decision cannot be put on to him but must rest with them.

The Anglican and the Roman Churches both look upon insemination with donated semen as being immoral, although they permit insemination of the wife with her husband's semen. This book is not concerned with sexual morality or with the ethics of insemination, but only with the effect which the latter has on the stability of the marriage and, looked at from this standpoint only, there can be no doubt that Artificial Insemination with Donated Semen, (A.I.D. as it is called), has brought happiness into many homes. Instead of imperilling marriages, it has salvaged marriages which otherwise would have broken up owing to the absence of a family. The fact that the husband has put aside all his personal prejudices against insemination in order that his wife may have what she desires more than anything else in the world, a child of her own, usually has the effect of drawing husband and wife more closely together. In view of this it is a pity that those who sincerely believe that A.I.D. is morally wrong should not have rested content with basing this belief on morality alone. They would have been in a much stronger position if they had done so, and to make statements to the effect that A.I.D. produces harmful psychological re-actions on the couple and that it is likely to disrupt the marriage is not only untrue but prejudicial to their case. Wrong is wrong, whatever the consequences of it may be, so why should people who are following the dictates of their conscience feel it to be necessary to bolster up their position with spurious arguments?

Several questions are likely to be asked by those who are making enquiries on the subject of insemination, and the com-monest one is about the health and character of the donor. Quite naturally they ask what guarantee they can have as to the health, the character and the constitution of the man who is to be the actual father of their child? All that it is possible to tell them is that they can be given no guarantee on this subject but must be content with the fact that the very few gynæcologists who carry out A.I.D. take their special work very conscientious-ly, and that none of them ever consents to perform insemination unless he believes that the wife and the husband concerned are potentially good parents. Nor will they agree to bring a baby into the world unless they consider the marriage to be a stable one. This being so, the enquiring couple will have to accept on trust the fact that the donors have been very carefully selected with regard to health and breeding. They can also be told that many of the donors are the fertile husbands of wives who have previously been successfully treated by the gynæcologists for infertility, husbands who now show gratitude for their own children in this way. It is essential, of course, that the actual identity of the donor should never be revealed, and that the donor should be equally ignorant of the destinations of his semen. The need for this secrecy is so obvious that it requires no explaining.

Another question frequently asked is: "What does insemination entail for the wife?" The answer to this is a very simple one. All that is required of her is that she should make a monthly pilgrimage to the consulting room of the gynæcologist in question in order to have a small quantity of highly fertile semen placed in the right position at the entrance to the womb. The visit will take up about half an hour of her time and she will suffer no pain. But it is impossible to foretell how many visits will be required and she will have to be prepared, if necessary, to continue her monthly visits for a year.

Should the procedure prove successful, as it is likely to prove if the wife is fertile, the child will have to be registered at the office of the Registrar of Births soon after it is born. This registration is usually done by the father and it will be for the husband to decide what name he will inscribe in the allotted place. Up till that moment only four people are likely to know of the fact that A.I.D. has been carried out on the wife, namely, the husband, the wife, the family doctor and the gynæcologist. Unless titles or entailed estates are involved, it would seem a pity that at this stage of the proceedings more people should be allowed in to the secret.

One final point has to be noted. There has been so much discussion about the ethics of A.I.D. and so many strong feelings have been expressed on the subject that no hospital clinic dares to undertake it, and this means that insemination cannot possibly be done under the Health Act. Moreover, very few gynæcologists are interested in A.I.D. or are equipped for carrying it out, and this makes the treatment exceedingly difficult to obtain. No actual figures can be given for the number of medical men actually using this method, but I should be surprised if there were as many as ten doctors in the whole of Great Britain who are willing and capable of carrying it out skilfully.

There is, of course, much less difficulty in getting the other form of insemination, A.I.H. (Insemination with the husband's semen) performed, owing to the fact that the Churches no longer regard it as immoral. The condition for which it is most frequently used is impotence of the husband, either partial or complete. When a marriage has remained unconsummated owing to incompetence on the side of the husband, the question is sometimes asked whether insemination would not be a good form of treatment on the grounds that it may relieve the husband of some of his anxiety and thus facilitate his cure. It is quite true that anxiety is a potent factor in impotence, and that the mere fact that an impotent husband is depriving his wife of all chance of conceiving is likely to increase his anxiety still further. If therefore he can be relieved of this load on his mind, he will approach the sexual act with much less concern and consequently will be more likely to succeed in it. But before A.I.H. is adopted, the gynæcologist will have to satisfy himself that the marriage is a reasonably stable one, for otherwise the happiness of the future child is likely to be imperilled.

A.I.H. should never be adopted lightheartedly, for although it helps in one way, it can hinder in other ways. Many marriages which have started with great sexual difficulties have to be dissolved later, and there will be much less difficulty in obtaining an annulment if it is a childless marriage. Moreover, a child obtained from a marriage by means of A.I.H. is rendered illegitimate by its subsequent annulment, even although it was the husband who provided the semen for the insemination. The moral obligations attached to a marriage are, of course, greatly increased by the existence of a young child, for divorce between a childless couple is one thing and a divorce between two people who have a young child is another thing. Many considerations have, therefore, to be taken into account before the remedy of A.I.H. is employed. It demands as careful a reviewing of all the factors concerned as does that other form of insemination, A.I.D.

I have written at considerable length on this controversial subject, partly because it is of growing importance, and partly in order to correct any impression which a reader may have that the few medical men and women who treat childlessness in this way carry on their work without a due sense of responsibility. On the contrary, they are fully aware of the seriousness of their actions, and are particularly trustworthy and conscientious people.

Another question which needs to be discussed is the ideal size for a family. This question is one which has only become of practical importance since the beginning of this century. In previous centuries children were given by God, and often taken away by God with equal rapidity, a truth revealed by the fact that though births were extremely numerous, the size of the population in this country remained almost stationary. As Havelock Ellis has put it: "In old family records we see two or even three brothers of the same name. 'John' was christened and 'John' died, so that name was available for a later 'John', and if he died, for a third." It was indeed fortunate that the infantile death rate was so high for no country could have produced sufficient food to support so large a number of people had all these children survived.

The question of what should be the size of the family can be approached from two directions, from that of the parents and from that of the nation and the latter aspect of the subject will be discussed first. It has been calculated that an average of 2·5 children would be required in order to maintain and to provide for a reasonable increase in the population of Great Britain, and by the term "reasonable increase" is meant reasonable from the standpoint of Great Britain's economics. At the present time this average size of a family is being maintained, for the number of children in the family is now somewhere between two and three. In certain families we find three or even four children, whilst in others there are only one, two or no children.

But the question of the ideal number of children must also be viewed from the standpoint of the individual family and particularly from the standpoint of the mother. Viewed from this angle the reduction in the average number of children has proved of immense benefit. The family is a biological unit but it can also be regarded as being a cultural unit, which is capable of exercising a considerable influence on society and it is for this reason that the family has sometimes been called the " unit of civilization". But prior to the family planning era the energies of the family were so engaged in the never-ending work of reproduction that little energy was left over for any civilizing action of this kind. This was particularly true of the mother of the family. It has been estimated that if left to nature a woman who is living in a healthy environment and who is married to a fertile husband will produce an average of fifteen children and it is obvious that if she be allowed to have so large a family she will have very little time left over for cultural activities in the wider environment of social life. Moreover the women of those days were so ill-educated that unless they happened to be specially gifted they had little to contribute to society.

Contrast with this the state of the modern mother of a family. It is quite true that in order to produce an average of 2·5 children much time and work will be demanded of her but it will not demand everything of her. Moreover the mother of today has received a much better education and has a great deal more to contribute to society than had the mothers of half a century ago. Modern mothers are also assisted to undertake outside work by the establishment of day nurseries. The facilities for parking the children of working mothers appear to be greater in some countries than in Great Britain and particularly in Russia where mothers of families are strongly encouraged to work on the land and in the factories. Lenin once boasted that "every kitchen maid must learn to rule the State". It was the kind of statement demagogues are fond of but it indicates the Communist Party's attitude to female labour.

The employment of women in part-time duties outside the home is certainly to be encouraged. A large percentage of school-teachers in this country are married women, some with children of their own, and there can be no doubt that women with sexual and maternal experience are particularly well equipped for handling school problems. Their scholastic attainments may not be very high but they are more likely to possess an instinctive understanding of children and their difficulties. Married women, and particularly married women with children, make admirable teachers.

14

THE PHYSIOLOGY OF
REPRODUCTION

ANATOMY is the science which deals with the structure of the body and physiology describes the way in which it works. Anatomy and physiology are therefore complementary studies to each other. It will, of course, be realized that the reproductive organs cannot discharge their functions properly without the co-operation of many other systems of organs in the body, the heart and blood vessels, the respiratory system, the digestive system, etc. These are essential to the maintainance of life, whereas the reproductive system is only essential to the continuation of the species. But although the reproductive organs are not necessary to the life of the individual their state may have a great effect on his or her health. As we shall see later the primary sex glands and the testicles and the ovaries form certain hormones or internal secretions which are absorbed into the blood stream and are necessary for the full development of the mind and the body and for the maintenance of health and vigour.

The male reproductive organs will be considered first. The external reproductive organs in the male are the testes (or testicles) and the phallus or penis. See page 199. The two testicles are originally developed within the abdomen but shortly before birth they emigrate outside the body and settle down in the scrotum or bag of skin in which they lie suspended. The reason for their emigration from the abdomen is an interesting one. It is that the testicles do their work better—the important work of producing spermatozoon—at a temperature a degree or two lower than that existing within the abdomen. Sometimes the testicles fail to descend and remain within the abdomen or else are arrested half-way in the region of the groin. This condition is known as cryptochism and it is one of the causes of male

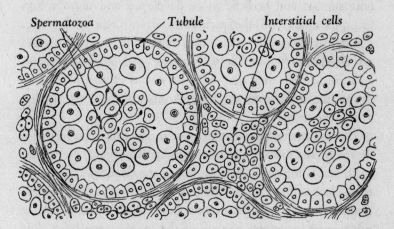

Spermatozoa   *Tubule*   *Interstitial cells*

HOW MALE CELLS ARE PRODUCED

Section of a testis enlarged many times, showing spermatozoa being formed in the seminiferous tubules. Between the tubules are the interstitial cells which manufacture the internal secretions concerned with the other male characteristics—growth of hair, shape of body and deeper voice register.

sterility. No spermatozoa are produced by retained testicles. In many cases testicles of this kind can be brought down into the scrotum by a surgical operation, but although this removes the discomfort associated with misplaced testicles it does not usually cure the sterility.

When we examine the testis under the microscope we find that it is made up of a large number of thread-like canals or tubules known as seminiferous tubules. These are lined with several layers of special cells whose function it is to produce a multitude of spermatozoa. These are budded off by special cells and are shed into the fluid secreted by other cells in the tubules. This fluid, heavily charged with spermatozoa, passes next into the much coiled canal, many feet in length, attached to the side of the testicle and known as the epididymis. There they receive nourishment and become more developed and more active. From the epididymis the spermatozoa pass into the vas deferens, a muscular channel by which they eventually reach the urethra and the outside world. The walls of the vas deferens are muscular in order that they may help, by means of contractions, to propel the fluid from the testicles onwards into the urethra during the sexual act.

The urethra or uro-genital passage (so called because it is shared by the urinary and the reproductive organs) pierces the penis and is the channel along which the ejaculation of semen takes place at the climax of the sexual act. What passes along the urethra at that time is a composite fluid called semen, which is a mixture of secretions, namely of the spermatozoa-laden fluid coming from the testicles and of secretions from what are known as the accessory sex glands, the chief of which are the prostate and the seminal vesicles. The two seminal vesicles are situated where the two vasa deferentes pierce the prostate in its passage into the urethra. These glands discharge a thick viscid secretion into the urethra where it mingles with other accessory secretions.

The prostate is a solid gland surrounding the urethra at its junction with the bladder and it is a source of much trouble to elderly men. This trouble arises from its becoming enlarged and pressing on the urethra, so that it impedes the evacuation of urine from the bladder. The function of the prostate is to produce a secretion which helps to cleanse the urethra of any residue of acid urine prior to the ejaculation of the semen and also nourishes and promotes movement of the spermatozoa. A third pair of glands which secrete fluid and add their secretions to the semen are known as Cowper's glands. These accessory glands are situated just below the prostate.

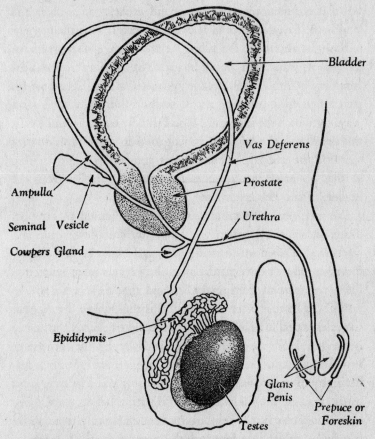

SECTION OF MALE REPRODUCTIVE ORGANS

Spermatozoa are manufactured in the testes, travel along the vas deferens, and are stored in the seminal vesicles. Secretions which increase the mobility of the spermatozoa are produced in the seminal vesicles and prostate gland.

The penis has the two-fold function of conducting urine from the bladder to the exterior and of conveying that precious fluid the semen, on which the continuation of the race depends, into the female passages. Because of this duality of function its structure has to be a complicated one. When performing the first or urinary function the penis, is a flaccid, flexible organ but when it is functioning in the second capacity it hardens and lengthens, in other words it becomes erect. This change in it is brought about by the filling of the sponge-like cavernous tissue in its walls with blood. In a state of sexual excitement the vascularity of the organ greatly increases and the nerves which are concerned in bringing about erection shut the venous gateways by which the incoming blood usually escapes. And whilst the penis and the urethra are engaged in their reproductive function the urinary function is put completely out of action, so that no urine is able to escape into the urethra from the bladder during the sexual act.

The nervous mechanism regulating the genital function of the genito-urinary system is of a highly complex nature and reference has been made to it in Chapter Nine. In that chapter it was stated that the centres controlling coitus were situated in the lower part of the spinal cord and that they were two in number. The first or erection centre is responsible for the first stages in sexual intercourse and the second or ejaculation centre is responsible for the final stage or the throwing out of the seed. It was pointed out that impotence in the male is the result of disharmony in the working of these two centres and that the most usual explanation of a lack of co-ordination between the spinal centres is the arrival of inhibiting impulses coming from above (the brain) which interfere with the work of the cord centres.

The female reproductive organs, unlike those of the male, lie almost entirely within the female's abdomen. These female organs consist of the ovaries, the Fallopian tubes, the uterus or womb and the vagina. See page 202. The ovaries are paired glands lying in the lower part of the abdominal cavity, that is to say the part to which the name pelvis is given. A broad band of tissue, called the broad ligament, stretches across the pelvis from one side to the other side, and to it are attached the ovaries, the Fallopian tubes and the uterus.

A microscopic examination of the ovaries shows them to be composed of two sorts of tissue, a ground or connective tissue and scattered throughout this a number of islands of large reproductive cells known as Graafian follicles. The smallest of these islands of reproductive cells possess no cavities but are solid masses made up of a central egg-cell or ovum surrounded by rows of round cells. Throughout the reproductive life of the female a constant activity is going on amongst these follicles. They increase in size and as they do so fluid is formed within them which creates a space between the centrally placed ovum and the circles of cells which surround the ovum. So large may a ripening follicle thus become that it may occupy a considerable part of a section made through the ovary. As the follicle matures it comes nearer and nearer to the surface of the ovary.

In those animals which produce large litters a number of follicles come to maturity simultaneously so that the ovary has the appearance of a bunch of grapes but in women only one ovum, as a rule, ripens each month. It has been calculated that during the whole of her reproductive life, extending say between the ages of fifteen and forty-five, a woman produces in her ovaries about four hundred mature eggs.

Each month a ripened follicle comes to the surface of the ovary, ruptures and discharges its egg cell into the pelvis in the neighbourhood of the expanded end of one of the two Fallopian tubes. After the ovum has been discharged the cells of the now empty follicle start dividing rapidly to form a yellow pigmented body known as the *corpus luteum*. The function of this yellow body will be discussed later.

The two Fallopian tubes or oviducts open on to the pelvic cavity near the ovaries. They end in trumpet-like expansions which are of assistance in catching the discharged ova. It is said that these trumpet-like expansions become more open and erect at the time of ovulation in order to assist in capturing the released ova. The Tubes are about four inches in length and they terminate in the two upper angles of the oblong shaped uterus.

The uterus lies in the pelvis just behind the bladder. In many animals it is branched but in a woman it is a single hollow

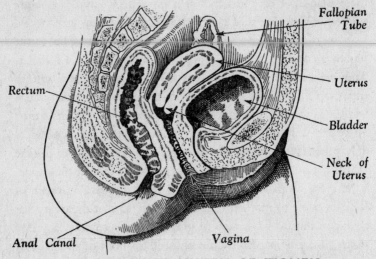

REPRODUCTIVE SYSTEM OF WOMEN

This cross-section shows the female reproductive organs in relation to the surrounding organs.

organ in which the child lies during the whole of pregnancy. The virgin uterus is about three inches long but it is an organ which has an immense capacity for enlargement. The lower extremity of the womb juts into the vagina and this lower jutting end of it is known as the cervix. A section across the uterus reveals a central cavity lined by a mucus membrane which is richly studded with glands. Outside this innermost mucus layer of the uterus are a number of muscular layers and beyond these muscular coats the smooth glistening covering of the peritoneum.

The vagina or passage into the outer world extends from the cervix to the large external folds of skin known as the labia majora, or greater lips. The vagina is lined by mucus membrane which is thrown into folds but the vaginal mucous membrane contains no glands of its own. The vaginal secretions are provided by the glands of the cervix and by two special glands, placed at the entry in the vagina and known as Bartholin's glands.

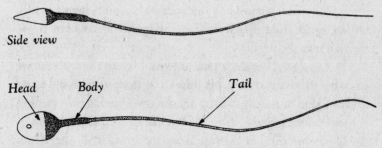

Side view

Head   Body   Tail

Front view

MALE SEX CELL MAGNIFIED

These diagrams show the side and front views of the male sex cell (spermatazoon), which consists of a head, containing the nucleus, and a long whip-like tail. The tail thrashes about, thus enabling the cell to travel in the fluid of the vagina and womb. After fertilization it has no further use and drops off.

Pregnancy depends on a spermatozoon and an ovum meeting together and coalescing. At the climax of the sexual act millions of spermatozoa are thrown into the vagina and fertilization takes place if one of these succeeds in making the perilous journey up through the cervical canal into the uterus and thence into the Fallopian tubes. This long journey is made partly under the spermatozoon's own mobile power, partly through the agency of the muscles of the uterus and partly by the sweeping action of the "cilia" or thread-like motile structures found on the lining of the Fallopian tubes. But in order to understand this act of fertilization by the spermatozoon something has to be said about the finer structures of this mobile male cell.

Seen under the microscope a spermatozoon closely resembles a tadpole. See page 203. It is made up of a flattish head, a short connecting piece or body and a very long tail which is in constant motion. It whips from side to side and propels the streamlined head and body forward. The spermatozoon has a long and dangerous journey to make, and it is because of this danger and because the odds against any one spermatozoon being successful are so great, that many millions of spermatozoa have to be thrown into the vagina.

The female sex organs which are visible from the exterior are the labia majora and the labia minora. If these greater and lesser folds of skin are separated by the fingers the vaginal opening comes into view and in front of this can be seen the opening of the female urethra. or passage from the bladder. In the virgin the vaginal opening is surrounded by the hymen and at the upper or front end of the vulva lies the small, solid, rod-like structure known as the clitoris. This female analogue of the male penis contains erectile tissue and is covered also by a fold of skin resembling a prepuce. The skin lying between the vulva in front and the anus, or opening of the bowel, behind is known as the perineum. It is this structure of muscle and skin which is so liable to be torn during child-birth.

In order to understand what happens after the spermatozoon and the ovum have met and fused, it will be necessary to study also the monthly changes taking place in the uterus, changes which constitute what is known as the menstrual cycle. This cycle can be divided into four chief stages. (1) A constructive stage in which the lining of the uterus is engaged in active growth and which lasts about twelve days; (2) a destructive stage of variable intensity during which blood vessels give way

and bleeding occurs; (3) an active stage of repair or regenera-
tion during which the bleeding stops and the mucus membrane
is completely restored; and (4) a stage of quiescence. All of these
changes are preparatory to fertilization and are the means by

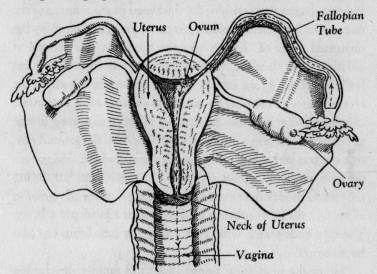

DISCHARGE OF AN OVUM

Each month an ovum ripens and bursts from the ovary, finding its way
into the Fallopian tube. If it is fertilized by a spermatozoon on its journey
through the tube to the womb, pregnancy begins. If not, it passes into the
womb and is discharged through the vagina during menstruation.

which the lining of the uterus is renewed each month and
brought into a suitable state for nidation; that is to say, for the
nourishment of the ovum should fertilization take place.

The monthly process of rupture of the follicle and discharge
of the ovum into the pelvis is known as "ovulation" and ovulation is controlled by hormones or chemical messengers circu-
lating in the blood. As has already been said, a yellow body
known as the corpus luteum forms in the empty follicle after
the ovum has been discharged from it and if conception should
occur this yellow body persists during the whole of the preg-

nancy. If conception does not take place the unfertilized ovum is expelled from the uterus in various discharges and the corpus luteum rapidly regresses and disappears.

When an ovum has been fertilized it first attaches itself to, and then buries itself within, the thickened mucous lining of the uterus which has been specially prepared for its reception by the menstrual cycle of changes. By the time that this process of nidation takes place the ovum has already started to divide but it divides much more rapidly after it has attached itself to the uterine mucous membrane, so quickly that it soon becomes a conglomeration of cells. At first the embryo is a very simple structure resembling a mulberry, but very soon the ground plan of a body is laid down within it. At the end of the first month the embryo is only about a quarter of an inch long but during the second month development has become sufficiently great to allow of a distinction being made between a head and a body. The tiny buds which will eventually grow into limbs can also be made out.

One of the interesting things about this rapidly developing embryo is that it goes through all the stages that have been passed through by man during the millions of years of his evolution. For example, during the second and third months the human embryo displays the gill-slits and the gills of its very remote ancestor, the fish, and at a much later stage it possesses the tail of its much less remote ancestors who lived in trees.

We must also examine the coverings of the developing embryo, for these play an important part in its nourishment. The mother provides the conditions required for the growth of the embryo within her womb in several different ways. Not only have food and oxygen to be supplied to the embryo but it is equally important that its waste products should be removed and these dual requirements are met through an interchange between the maternal and the embryonic bloods. This does not mean that maternal blood passes from the mother into the embryo and then back again. What actually happens is that a special organ is formed between the two in which the blood of the mother is brought sufficiently close to the blood of the embryo to allow of an interchange of nourishing material and waste products. This intervening organ is the placenta and a microscopic examination of its structure shows that all that separates the two circulatory systems of mother and child is a single layer of flattish cells.

The placenta is composed of two parts, one derived from the embryo and the other contributed by the mother. In the earliest stages of its development the embryonic portion of the placenta forms a hollow bag in which the embryo hangs suspended by a short stalk, but in course of time the stalk lengthens and becomes the umbilical cord. This cord contains many blood vessels which are connected up with the mother's circulatory system. The size, both of the embryo and of the uterus, increases with great rapidity. By the third month of pregnancy the uterus can just be felt above the pubis or front bone of the pelvic girdle. The first feeble movements of the developing child are felt by the mother between the fourteenth and the sixteenth weeks of pregnancy, and by the twenty-eighth week the fœtus becomes viable; in other words it is accepted as being capable of living on its own, should it be born. During the whole of the sojourn in the womb the developing child lies curled up within its coverings, with the arms and legs flexed and folded up in front of it. At birth the average length of the child is twenty inches and the average weight seven and a half pounds for a boy and seven pounds for a girl.

As has previously been stated, the reproductive systems of both sexes are influenced very strongly by the internal secretion of the ductless glands. They are controlled above all by the hormones secreted by the primary glands of sex (the testes and the ovaries) and by the hormones coming from the pituitary gland (the master-gland which lies within the skull and at the base of the brain). It is believed that the pituitary gland produces two primary hormones which have an action on the primary sex glands and stimulate the development of the spermatozoa and of the ova. The other pituitary secretion promotes the growth of the corpus luteum in the female. The pituitary produces additional hormones which stimulate the growth of the breasts and promotes the secretion of milk. Finally a hormone has been found in the pituitary which stimulates the growth of the testicles and the ovaries and thus assists the development of the reproductive system. With all these activities going on within its substance it is not surprising that the pituitary is known as the master-gland of the endocrine circle.

Pregnancy is associated with other body changes, with the cessation of menstruation, with "morning sickness" which usually occurs from the second to the third or fourth month, and sometimes with a slight enlargement of the thyroid gland in the neck. But the most marked changes are those occurring in the mammary or milk glands. The breasts start swelling quite early in pregnancy although milk does not appear in them until the second to the fifth day after birth.

The woman's body has an astonishing capacity for accommodating itself to the great changes brought about by pregnancy so that being pregnant does not of necessity involve great discomfort. On the contrary, some women enjoy a sense of well-being during pregnancy which they do not experience at other times. The average duration of pregnancy is estimated at two hundred and eighty days or ten lunar months.

During the later stages of pregnancy, and particularly during the final weeks, the uterus becomes more irritable and occasional contractions pass over it. With the actual approach of labour these contractions become stronger and much more frequent and the fœtal membranes, distended with fluid, are forced down into the cervix. Sometimes this stretching process gives rise to a little bleeding. The next event is the contraction of the longitudinally placed muscle fibres of the uterus, contractions which tend to open the cervical canal. These contractions mark the beginning of parturition, or the process of giving birth, an act in which the body of the uterus, the cervical canal and the vagina become a continuous and open passage. The fœtal membranes commonly rupture about this time, the rupture being signalled by the sudden escape of fluid from the uterus and vagina. In the second stages of labour the child is expelled from the uterus into the vagina and thence into the external world. This expulsion is brought about by the vigorous contractions of the uterus aided by the muscles of the abdomen and the diaphragm. The vagina is extremely elastic and the passage of the child through it is assisted by a copious flow of mucus.

At the beginning of labour the pains occur at intervals of about fifteen to thirty minutes, but they soon become more frequent, until they may attain a frequency of one every two minutes. In a completely normal parturition the head is expelled first and this is rapidly followed by the expulsion of the body and legs. When twins are born the second child is usually born about half an hour after the first but a longer delay is not uncommon. In the third stage of labour the placenta and the membranes are delivered.

Twins have always been, and still are, a subject of great interest to mankind. There are two kinds of twins, namely twins which are the result of the simultaneous fertilization of two ova and twins which arise from the splitting of a single fertilized ovum into two separate halves, which eventually develop into two different individuals. Twins of this Tweedledum and Tweedledee variety, so similar in their appearance that nobody except their mother can distinguish the one from the other, are invariably of the same sex. The other variety of twins coming from the formation of two ova and their fertilization at about the same time may be either of the same or of different sexes and they may resemble each other no more closely than do ordinary brothers and sisters. Indeed that is all that these twins really are, brothers or sisters conceived and born within a few hours of each other.

It is the former type of twin arising out of the splitting of a single fertilized ovum which was of such interest to the scientist Francis Galton, the gifted kinsman of Charles Darwin. He suggested, a century ago, that the study of identical twins—as this particular variety of twins is called—might throw light on how much we are the products of our heredity and how much of our upbringing and what the geneticist likes best to study is identical twins who have been parted soon after birth and brought up in different surroundings.

Strange and interesting stories have been told of such twins keeping step with each other throughout childhood, youth and middle-age, contracting the same illnesses about the same time, developing similar temperaments and tastes, and in one instance being arrested simultaneously for similar misdemeanours. "Heredity decides everything and upbringing is of little account," declare the narrators of these interesting stories.

But a critical survey of the scientific literature of identical twins suggests that the case for nature has been overstated. When we peruse the life histories of the four pairs of identical twins, Clara and Doris, Earl and Frank, Gertrude and Helen, and James and Keith recorded in *Psychological Monographs, Vol.* 63, we do not find so close a resemblance between them as some other writers on this subject have claimed. Upbringing had a very marked effect on the character of these four twins, and this is in harmony with my own limited experience of identical twins.

"I and my twin sister are individuals and not just replicas of each other," said one very intelligent identical twin to me. "We are very great friends, but now that we are grown up we could not possibly live together. When we die, we shall die of the same disease, for identical twins always do."

Occasionally an accident happens and the original splitting of the fertilized ovum is incomplete, so that Siamese twins are born, united in a variety of ways. Or the more severe accident occurs that one of the twins develops entirely at the expense of the other, so that in the end it outgrows and completely envelops it. From time to time, a surgeon is called upon to remove from a patient a tumour known as a dermoid cyst, and this tumour contains a queer assortment of human tissue, wisps of hair, and fragments of teeth, cartilage, bones and skin. The most plausible way of accounting for this rag-bag of human tissues is that it represents a twin brother or sister who, from the very beginning, has never had the chance of developing properly. It is, in short, a permanently suppressed brother or sister twin.

At one time an expectant mother, who from her largeness suspected that she was going to have twins, was compelled to wait until the later months of pregnancy to have this suspicion confirmed or refuted, but nowadays the diagnosis can be made much earlier by means of an X-ray. This will show the presence or not of two skulls and backbones and thus allow of a diagnosis being reached long before the doctor can decide this matter by palpating the mother's abdomen and by listening with his stethoscope for the beating of two fœtal hearts.

There are other reasons for a woman's womb being bulkier than is usual at this particular stage of pregnancy and a common one is an excess of fluid in the membrane surrounding the developing fœtus. One more statement can be made about twins and that is that the tendency to bear twins seems to be a hereditary trait. Triplets, quadruplets and quintuplets are such rare phenomena that they need not be considered in this book.

15

HEREDITY

IT was said in Chapter Five that few people took into consideration heredity and eugenics when they were about to become engaged and that it was quite natural that mutual attraction should at that time take precedence of everything else. The young man in love cannot be expected to pause and wonder whether the girl he adores is likely to make a good mother and it would be too much to ask of the girl who is responding to his advances that she should have similar thoughts about him. Yet the health and the breeding of the future children are going to be of vital importance to them both in the years to come, and in a book which is devoted to Love, Marriage and the Family the question of heredity and the laws which control the handing down of qualities from the parents to their children should surely find a place. The present chapter will therefore be devoted to these subjects.

Heredity is not only of great importance but also of great interest to us. In Maeterlinck's play *The Betrothed* there is a scene in which all the ancestors, right back into the misty past, appear and dance round the young couple, proclaiming their history and telling them what they have contributed to them, the present generation. Of what immense interest would it be to each of us if our ancestors were to return in a similar way and were to tell us what gifts and advantages, what handicaps and disadvantages, each had contributed to our general make-up.

But before we discuss the laws of heredity there is a preliminary question to be answered. To which should we attribute the greater importance in the development of a person's characteristics, heredity or upbringing? This is a question which has often been asked by parents and a question to which the experts have given different answers. One kind of expert, and usually the expert with biological leanings, has made extravagant claims for the importance of heredity, and others, such as the psychologists, have been equally emphatic about the influence of upbringing on the child. A Jesuit was so sure about his ability to mould by upbringing a child's mind to his will that he once said: "Give me a child to rear until the age of five and afterwards you can do anything you like with him." And without doubt these early formative years of life are of immense importance in the development of character. Freud laid the greatest stress on these early years in a child's life when discussing character and the genesis of neuroses and other functional disorders.

But the geneticists are equally confident that were they to be given complete charge of the human race and, more particularly, of the marriage arrangements of humanity, they would be able to breed a super-race of man. According to J. B. S. Haldane they could produce by means of selective breeding a man who would be able to think like Newton, to write like Racine, to paint like Van Eyck, to compose like Bach. He would be as incapable of hatred as St. Francis and when death came at the end of his life, he would meet it with as little fear as Captain Oates.

I am not a geneticist but personally I am of the opinion that Haldane has exaggerated what can be done by means of breeding and that no experiment of this kind on the human race, however grand its scale and however long it lasted, would be able to produce a man who combined in his person so many excellent qualities, some of which would probably prove to be incompatible with others. It is quite true that blood is of great importance and that there are such things as highly musical families and also families of highly gifted business men. There are also families which have produced an exceptionally high percentage of brilliant individuals, such as the Cecil family, the Russells and the Darwins, the Wedgwoods, the Galtons and the Keynes families. But who shall say to what extent the achievements of these gifted families were due to inheritance and to what extent they can be explained by the favourable environment in which their children were brought up.

Let us take Bertrand Russell as an example of a man who has come of an exceedingly clever stock. He probably owes a great deal to his heredity, for his mother was a Stanley and his father a Russell, both exceptionally clever families. But what immense advantages the young Bertrand Russell was given as a child. From babyhood onwards he was surrounded by exceptionally clever people, and when his parents died at a comparatively early age, he was sent to be brought up at 10 Downing Street, where his grandfather lived as Prime Minister. And his grandfather brought him into contact with the most distinguished figures of the Victorian Age. He was often to be seen sitting at the Downing Street dining-table where he could listen to conversations which rich men would have given thousands of pounds to hear. He listened to politicians debating on State policy, to scientists discoursing on science, and to artists, writers and musicians talking about the arts. How much does the now elderly and exceedingly brilliant Lord Russell owe to his heredity and how much is it due to the exceptional character of his upbringing? It is quite impossible to draw any line between these two influences.

What is true of Lord Russell is true also of the children of the so-called musical families. From their earliest days the children of these families have been brought up in a very favourable environment, have heard music played and discussed throughout the day and gone to sleep at night with the strains of the violin and the piano ascending from below stairs to mingle with their dreams. Any exceptional musical ability they may have later displayed was therefore the result of two things, the inheritance from their forebears of certain musical potentialities and dispositions and the nurturing of these inherited gifts by an exceptionally favourable environment. Nature and nurture have been equally responsible for any musical success they may later have achieved.

It is difficult to unravel heredity from environment for the two are working hand in hand in the development of a child's potentialities. But in discussing the inheritance of intelligence and of other psychological qualities, it is necessary to be quite clear as to what a child actually inherits. He does not so much inherit a trait as the capacity to develop that trait provided that the right environment to its development is given him. If the environment is quite unsuitable for this, then the inherited potentiality will not be developed. For example, many European children who inherited good material from their parents have remained stunted throughout their lives owing to the fact that they were brought up in concentration camps in totalitarian countries at a critical period in their development. Fortunately the "genes" or vehicles by which hereditary qualities are handed on to the next generation, are highly resistant to outside forces and although these starved children are now rather stunted and poorly developed adults, they will be able to pass on to their children the capacity to develop faculties which have remained undeveloped in themselves. In the same way, children whose intellectual potentialities have never had an opportunity to mature will be able to hand on to their children a similar capacity to develop a high degree of intelligence for the seed of intelligence is there, awaiting an opportunity to grow and bring forth fruit.

Genetics is the science which tries to explain why children

resemble their parents and at the same time differ from them. In other words, it is the study of the transmission of qualities from one generation to another, and the man who laid the foundation for this new science was Gregor Johann Mendel, the priestly son of an Austrian farmer. At the age of twenty-one the young Mendel entered a monastery at Brünn as a novice and three years later he was ordained a priest. The experiments which he carried out in the monastery garden and which were to provide the foundations for the future science of genetics are of such importance to an understanding of heredity that they will have to be described in detail.

For his earlier experiments the Abbé Mendel chose two varieties of pea, one of which grew to a height of six feet and the other which never reached a greater height than two feet. He first studied for a long time the characteristics of these two varieties of pea and made sure that they always bred true to type, the dwarf pea giving rise only to the dwarf plants and the tall variety of pea only to the six-foot plants.

The question he then asked himself was: "What sort of off-spring would result if I were to fertilize the flowers of the tall variety pea with pollen from the short variety pea?" When he put this matter to a practical test, he found that the offspring were not, as he had rather expected them to be, peas which were intermediate in height but that they were all tall peas. Mendel realized that somehow or other the feature of tallness had overcome the feature of shortness, and he therefore called tallness in peas a "dominant" character, and shortness a "recessive" character. Geneticists still make use of these terms.

This led to his asking himself a second question: "What has happened to the recessive trait which has disappeared in this first new generation of peas?" He again put the matter to the test by fertilizing the first generation of peas, F_1, with their own pollen and he afterwards made a statistical study of the F_2

second generation of plants which resulted from this. He found
that although the recessive trait of shortness had disappeared in
the first F1 generation, it had not been lost, since it now reappeared in this new F2 generation. Approximately a quarter of
the F2 plants were short and although this recessive trait of
shortness had gone underground for a time it had not been
altered or in any way contaminated by its close association with
the dominant factor of tallness, for the short plants which had
reappeared possessed all their former characteristics. Indeed
when the F2 short plants were permitted to self-fertilize, they
continued to bring forth only short plants for many generations.

But it was quite otherwise with the F2 plants displaying the
dominant feature of tallness. These tall peas produced two varieties of offspring when they were self-fertilized; there was offspring which continued to give rise only to tall plants but there
was also offspring which behaved precisely as the F1 hybrids
had previously behaved, producing both tall and short offspring
in the ratio of 3 to 1. Mendel's results are shown in diagram-
matic form in the following table which has been taken from
L. Doncaster's work on Heredity. In this table "T" stands for
the tall factor, and "t" for its absence (shortness).

Original Parents		T x t			
F1 (First Generation)		Tt			
F2 (Second Generation)	TT		2Tt		tt
F3 (Third Generation)	TT	TT	2Tt	tt	tt

From this table it is clear that amongst the offspring of the F1
(hybrid) generation some (tt) have eliminated the tall factor
entirely, others (TT) have eliminated the short factor, and a
third group, which Mendel found to be twice as numerous as
the other two (hence recorded as 2Tt), continued to bring forth
mixed offspring on self-fertilization.

Similar results have been obtained from breeding experiments in animals. For example, when white rabbits are crossed with coloured rabbits, colour behaves as the dominant factor and whiteness as the recessive factor. With rough and smooth-haired guinea-pigs, roughness is dominant over smoothness, and amongst cattle the polled or hornless variety is dominant over the normal horned state.

When we turn to humanity to study the laws of heredity special difficulties occur. The experimental method for obvious reasons cannot be applied, but the careful examination of family records shows that dark hair and eyes behave as a dominant character, and fair hair and blue eyes as recessive. Tallness and shortness are, however, not transmitted in accordance with the law established by Mendel. If a tall man marries a short wife the sons are neither as tall as the father nor as short as the wife. Nor are the grandsons divided sharply, like Mendel's pea plants, into a tall group and a short group. There is rather a graded series ranging from tall to short. It is obvious, therefore, that there are different modes of inheritance, and that Mendel's discovery cannot be applied to all of the characteristics which parents hand down to their children and grandchildren.

Since direct experiment is not possible in the case of human beings, workers in this branch of science have had to rely on the statistical method of research. A definite physical peculiarity is chosen which can be observed in a large number of parents and offspring in order that some conclusion may be reached as to its transmission. The founder of this Statistical or, as it is now called, Biometrical, study of heredity was Sir Francis Galton, a cousin of Darwin's. As a result of his investigations Galton came to the conclusion that half of the heritage of an individual may be taken as being derived from the two parents, one-quarter from the four grandparents, one-eighth from the great grand-parents, and so on. Karl Pearson, the successor of Galton, working along the same lines, found that the parental bequest was greater, and the ancestral inheritance less than Galton had estimated, but that otherwise his conclusions were correct.

It must be remembered, however, that this Law of Ancestral Inheritance is true only when it is applied to a very large number of individuals taken as a whole mass, and that it is a statistical rather than a psychological law. It may not be true of all cases that the offspring are influenced at all by ancestors beyond the parents whilst in other cases these ancestors may have had important effects on the offspring. This being so it is possible only to say what is the *average* influence of the forebears of a given generation upon its offspring.

The statistical method of research has thrown light on a great many problems which previously admitted of no answer, for example, on the problem whether such gifts as great intellectual ability or even genius are inherited or not. Karl Pearson has investigated this question of the transmission of great intellectual ability by studying the class lists at Oxford. The investigation of the results obtained in the Oxford examinations by two thousand five hundred pairs of fathers and sons showed that a distinct correlation existed between their achievments. If the fathers took very high places in the examinations the sons also took high places and *vice-versa*, in a considerable percentage of cases. The agreement between the results obtained by a large number of brothers was even closer, a resemblance that was to be expected since brothers come from the same mothers as well as from the same fathers.

Unfortunately, what is true of intellectual ability also holds good for feeble-mindedness. Goddard found that heredity plays a leading part in the production of this deplorable condition. This was shown by the fact that of four hundred and eighty-two children born of forty-four feeble-minded couples, all except six were also feeble-minded.

The question is sometimes asked whether alcoholism is inherited and whether the offspring of drunken parents are likely to show feeble-mindedness. In this connexion, Stockard's experiments on animals are of interest. He subjected guinea-pigs every day to the action of alcohol vapour until they became intoxicated and he found, quite contrary to what he had expected, that they remained both healthy and fertile. But amongst their offspring a large proportion of defectives appeared, both in the first and in the subsequent generation, the commonest defects being abnormalities of the eyes and of the central nervous system. But the results obtained by Stockard must not be applied too glibly to the human race, for later experiments of a similar nature on mice, fowls and moths gave entirely different results. The evils of excessive drinking are obvious, but it has yet to be proved that physical and mental degeneration of the drunkard's descendants is amongst them.

Galton, the founder also of the science of eugenics, tried to estimate the relative importance of heredity and upbringing to a child by studying the behaviour of twins who had been removed from their parents soon after birth and brought up in different homes. In order that the heredity factors in the twins should be as equal as possible he selected for his study twins arising from the fertilization of a single ovum, or what are known as homologous twins. He found that such twins continued to resemble each other throughout their lives far more closely than did ordinary brothers and sisters, in spite of marked differences in their upbringing in different homes. Consequently he concluded that heredity played a greater part in determining character than did environment. But again we must accept these experimental results with reservations, for whilst Galton's conclusions may be true of a child's physical development they cannot be applied to a child's mental development. There can be little doubt that if the child of a brilliant father were to be handed over to the care of an illiterate tramp his intellectual development would suffer far more seriously from this change in his upbringing than would his physical development. Conversely if the child of the said illiterate tramp were to be brought up in the household of the brilliant man, his chances of becoming eminent would be far greater than were those of the tramp's foster child. In other words, mental qualities are more strongly influenced by environment than are physical qualities.

The last question which requires answering is how large a part heredity plays in the development of illnesses. Are many diseases transmitted by the parents to their offspring? First it must be pointed out that a great many of the illnesses from which we suffer are due to infection with viruses and micro-organisms, and it is obvious that such illnesses cannot be passed on from parent to child. In order to understand why not, it is necessary to know that hereditary characteristics are transmitted from one generation to another by means of minute structures known as genes. In the centre of all the cells which make up our bodies are to be found round condensations of protoplasm which are the organizers and controllers of the cell's manifold activities, structures which are known as nuclei. In order to render the constituents of cells more visible under the microscope, biologists stain them with various dyes, and the nucleus of a cell always stains more deeply with a dye than does the rest of it. If we examine the nucleus under a very high magnification we find that it is made up of a twisted filament resembling a skein of silk which, when the cell is about to divide down the middle to form two new cells, breaks up into a number of fragments called chromosomes. Along these chromosomes are strung a number of small bodies closely resembling the beads of a necklace and these are the genes or carriers of hereditary traits. Now the micro-organisms of infective illnesses are themselves cells which possess their own chromosomes and genes, and it would be ridiculous to suppose that such comparatively large bodies as micro-organisms could be transported to the child on the genes of ova and spermatozoa. No infective disease is ever inherited in the strict sense of that word.

"But what about the inheritance of tuberculosis and syphilis?" a reader may ask. The answer to this question is: "Neither of these diseases is inherited but they may both be contracted by a child very early in its life." The baby of a tubercular mother is constantly exposed to the bacillus of tuberculosis if the mother's tuberculosis is still active, and consequently it is very liable to contract the disease itself. In syphilis the disease can establish its hold on the child at a still earlier date through the placenta, whilst the child is still within the mother's womb. The baby, therefore, can be born with all the signs of congenital syphilis, yet the disease has not been transmitted through the mother's or the father's genes.

There are, however, diseases which can be inherited in this way by means of the genes, and the most striking of these is haemophilia, a hereditary disease in which the clotting power of the blood is deficient. One of the interesting characteristics of this family disease is that the males alone are affected, although the females may act as the means by which the disease is transmitted to the next generation. It is well known that the Hapsburg family has long suffered from this hereditary complaint of bleeding. There are other blood diseases also which are said to be hereditary, as well as certain forms of blindness, diseases associated with a loss of muscular power and diseases manifesting themselves in mental deterioration.

There are also examples of certain deficiencies being transmitted to the child which makes it more prone to develop a disease at a later date.

For example, one question which is sometimes asked: "Is cancer ever inherited?" Now, although there is still a great deal to be learnt about cancer, the answer to this question is probably in the affirmative with certain reservations. Not cancer itself but the tendency to cancer in later years may be inherited. Research workers on cancer are able to breed in their laboratories certain strains of mice which almost always die eventually of some form of cancer. It would seem therefore that the genes are involved in some way in this tendency of the mice to develop cancer, but in what way they are involved is not yet known. The same may be said also of diabetes, that although the disease itself is never inherited, some weakness in the body's chemistry may be passed on from the parents to the child, which renders it a little more likely to develop diabetes later on in life than another child born of non-diabetic parents. And what applies to diabetes probably applies also to some other diseases.

But it would be a mistake to jump too readily to the conclusion that a deficiency, a malformation or a predisposition is inherited. It cannot be assumed, for example, that because a mentally deficient child has been born, the trouble has necessarily been inherited.

The mother of a defective child may have been infected with the virus of German measles during the early months of her pregnancy, or she may have been exposed to the action of X-rays without proper precautions having been taken, or her diet during her pregnancy may have been deficient in some substance necessary to the proper development of the embryo's central nervous system. All of these events must be excluded before we have any right to say that the child has inherited its feeble-mindedness from its parents. Because we have so much to learn about hereditary influences in the development of disease, the advice of a competent authority should be taken before a couple come to the conclusion that because their family histories are bad it would be wiser that they should not have children.

16

DIFFICULTIES AND DANGERS
TO MARRIED LIFE

MARRIAGES are not made by higher authorities in heaven but
by ordinary men and women on this earth and, like all man-
made things, they are subject to many flaws and errors. For a
brief period, during the honeymoon perhaps, the young couple
may walk in a country remote from this ordinary world and are
free, for the time being, of all its cares and preoccupations. But
sooner or later they will have to come back to earth and to concern themselves with such wearisome things as tradesmen's
bills, kitchen boilers, things lost in the laundry, income tax
forms, colds in the head, and the rent due next quarter day.
Nor is it only with the demands of the external world that they
will have to contend, for there is an equally exacting inner
world which will have to be dealt with. They are two ordinary
human beings, full of odd whims and fancies, established habits
and prejudices, and subject like the rest of us to changing moods
and sudden irritations. It is no easy job, therefore, that these
two differently constituted people of opposite sexes have
undertaken, this job of living together for better or for worse,
in sickness and in health and for the rest of their lives.

But it can be done and it has actually been done by quite a
number of people who have deliberately set out to work towards this end. There will, of course, be many ups and downs
in this difficult creative task of theirs, moments of intense irritation, of snapping back at each other, of high dudgeon and

withdrawing, of pretence, and of shabby utterances, and of still shabbier thoughts. All these human mechanisms will make their task very difficult, but they can win through if they display sufficient science and skill. Science and skill will be required of them just as they are required for driving a car, yet the strange thing is that although everybody recognizes the need for these in car driving, comparatively few see the need for them in marriage management. But Adler saw this very clearly when he wrote that marriage was a constructive task of two people of opposite sex who were determined to "live together in order to relieve and enrich each other's lives." It is a good description of married life for it places emphasis where it is needed most, on the fact that successful marriages do not happen accidentally but have to be made.

And what creative work is better worth doing than this?Not that the highest grade of marriage-making is possible to everybody, for sometimes the raw material provided is of an inferior nature. R. L. Stevenson writes of these second grade marriages: "You have only to look these happy couples in the face, to see that they have never been in love, or in hate, or in any high passion, all their days. When you see a dish of fruit at dessert, you sometimes set your affections upon one particular peach or nectarine, watch it with some anxiety as it comes to the table, and feel quite a sensible disappointment when it is taken by someone else. I have used the phrase 'high passion'. Well, I should say that this was about as high a passion as generally leads to marriage. One husband hears after marriage that some poor fellow is dying of his wife's love. 'What a pity', he exclaims, 'you know I could so easily have got another.' And yet that is a very happy union. . . . Once more: a married lady was debating the subject with another lady. 'You know, my dear', said the first, 'after ten years of marriage, if he is nothing else, your husband is always an old friend'. . . . 'There is a common note in these illustrations of the modern idyll', continues R. L. Stevenson. "You wonder whether it was *always* equally dull and spiritless. . . . To deal plainly, if they only married when they fell in love, most people would die unwed; and amongst the others there would be not a few tumultuous households'," (R. L. Stevenson *Virginibus Puerisque*).

Stevenson's own rather uninspired marriage is reflected in these meditations of his and in what follows: "Marriage", he continues, "is comfortable, but it is not at all heroic. It contains narrows, and damps the spirits of generous men. In marriage a man becomes slack and selfish, and undergoes a fatty degeneration of his moral being. He is so comfortable and happy that he begins to prefer comfort and happiness to everything else on earth, his wife included . . . I am often filled with wonder that so many marriages are so passably successful and so few come to open failure, the more so as I fail to understand the principle on which people regulate their choice."

If Stevenson had written of marriage today he would scarcely have been able to say that "few marriages come to failure", for a great many of our modern marriages end in the divorce court. The woman of today demands much more of marriage than did Mrs. Stevenson, for woman has come into her own and is no longer forced as formerly to live in an entirely man-made world.

A modern marriage is a partnership between people of equal rights and there has to be much more give and take in the home than in Stevenson's time. Each half has to sacrifice certain individual liberties for the sake of the whole. Not that this sacrifice is invariably made, for there are still husbands who are as much the slaves of their business or their professional careers after marriage as they were before it, husbands who return to their homes at night too exhausted to be able to do anything more than nod their heads over evening papers and retire early to bed. It is small wonder that women married to such husbands find home life dull and seek more lively entertainment else-where. Formerly this use of the home as a rest-house was the prerogative of the male sex alone, but now that women have careers and are engaged in every form of business and profession, it is sometimes used by them for the same purposes.

In discussing the subject of how much time the husband and the wife are prepared to give to each other for the sake of the marriage, Oswald Schwarz points out that it is not so much the number of hours that the busier of the two partners is able to spare which counts as the mutual understanding and trust existing between them.

"The amount of time that husband and wife spend together is not material", he writes. "Their outside interests need not be identical. . . . . The bond that keeps the two together is the sense of belonging and sharing—nothing else. But if this bond does not exist a marriage is hollow and is held together only by accidental factors and external means which in themselves cannot carry the burden. Then it matters a great deal whether the woman has a quick drink with her colleague after office hours, instead of hurrying home. Trifling disagreements may grow into catastrophies when the essential and genuine trust is absent." (Oswald Schwarz, *The Psychology of Sex*. (Pelican).

It is the trifling disagreements which count for so much in married life and when we add them up they usually amount to a considerable sum. Jung has said that women are the high priestesses of small things, and by this he meant that whilst men usually see things as wholes, women are more disposed to see them as collections of details. The different ways in which they tackle problems should make men and women excellent part-ners, if they can only manage to work together. But this difference also explains why a wife is so upset by some com-paratively small error to which the husband has attributed no

importance at all. If, for example, he has wandered about the
house leaving a trail of ash and cigarette ends behind him, he
did so without any intention of hurting his wife's feelings, but
if she takes, as she almost certainly does, a great pride in her
house, she will feel personally affronted by his thoughtlessness.
So also is no harm intended by the wife when she insists on
turning out her husband's untidy study just as he is settling
down to write some important letters. Each places emphasis in
a different place, and each is upset by different things.

Three things are of the utmost importance in married life.
First, that the couple should get to know each other's peculiarities as soon as possible; second, that they should accept each
other's different ways of doing things; and third, that when
grievances do arise, as they undoubtedly will, these grievances
should be *ex*pressed and not *sup*pressed. Complaints resemble
weeds in that they grow best in the shade, and by brooding on
them they are transformed by the imagination of the brooder
into such fantastic shapes as to be no longer recognizable. This
being so, it is far better that the husband or the wife should be
told by the affronted partner what is the matter before the
grievance has had time to undergo this transformation.

Marriage difficulties and disharmonies resemble also illnesses
in that there are usually two stages in their development, an
acute stage and a chronic. The acute stage in a marital upset is
the stage in which both parties become aware of a state of inner
tension brought about by some difficulty which, so far, they
have been unable to resolve. Both are genuinely distressed to
think that the disharmonies which spoil other people's marriages
are also cropping up in their own, a marriage which they had
always believed to be quite out of the ordinary. For the successful treatment of this acute stage of the illness three things are
necessary.

First, both parties should realize that no marriage has ever been immune from marital difficulties; second, that they should agree to be outspoken and not to nurse their grievances in silence; and third, they should accept the fact that people's characters do not change suddenly as they are sometimes described as doing in the final chapters of novels. Because of this unchangeability, the two partners will have to work with each other as they *are* and give up trying to bring about mutual reforms. And this final requirement is, of course, the most important of them all. How seldom do we accept anybody as he or she is, with all his or her virtues, weaknesses, idiosyncracies and failings. "If only he were different, how much nicer he would be", we mutter. "If only she would talk a little less, what a relief it would be to us all", we exclaim. "If only he were better tempered, how much easier it would be for everybody concerned", we say. Now all of these inner protests of ours may be justified, but somehow or other we have to contrive to get along with these other people as they *are and not as we should like them to be*. It is in this shape that heredity and nurture have fashioned the people we are criticizing, and we have to get along with them as best we can. If any reform is to be done, then it can only be done with any likelihood of success on ourselves and we need it as much as anybody else.

Sometimes marital difficulties come from an entirely different direction, namely, from the direction of our imaginations. We rarely see people as they are, but view them through the distorting glasses of our imaginations, and the impressions the two partners have of each other at the beginning of married life are particularly likely to be incorrect. Many men carry in their hearts images of the ideal woman and wife, and still more women embark on marriage with imaginative portraits of the ideal man and husband. Now no great harm would be done if the owners kept these emblems of perfection locked up in their shrines but, unfortunately, they bring them out and project their images on to the ordinary individuals they happen to have married. Now it is difficult enough to live up to one's own ideals, but to be forced to imitate the ideals of other people is even more fatiguing and this is what these dreamers are expecting of their marriage partners. At the start the husband or wife, as the case may be, is flattered at being placed on a pedestal, but soon the situation becomes awkward and finally quite intolerable. Then comes the inevitable moment when the unwilling imposter crashes on to the floor and is seen to be what he or she really is, a very ordinary person with all the faults, stupidities and weaknesses of the ordinary person. Two cases from my own files illustrate what dangerous situations the imagination may create in married life.

The first is the case of a husband who came to see me with sexual difficulties and on the verge of a nervous breakdown. His wife accompanied him and after I had seen her husband she asked to speak to me about the situation, which she claimed to see very clearly. She described their marriage in ecstatic terms and told me that her husband could not bear to spend a single night away from home. Indeed, they were scarcely ever apart, and were entirely wrapped up in each other. "He's given up his club and all his old friends, and we are both quite miserable when we are not together". I watched the course of this marriage very carefully for several months and was at first puzzled by the husband's behaviour, which did not seem to fit in with what his wife had told me. Then I realized that the husband was not in the least what his wife imagined him to be, namely, a man so devoted to his home and his wife that he could not bear to be away from them. On the contrary, he was a man who was being suffocated by his wife's affection and possessiveness, a man who was longing to escape from them and who eventually did so and recovered his potency and health.

The second example of the mischief wrought by imagination had a more satisfactory ending. A recently married young man came to see me in order to discuss his sexual difficulties, and he talked to me about his wife much as a devout Catholic would have talked to me about his favourite saint. She was so pure and so soulful that I could not believe that she existed as a flesh and blood girl and obviously his wife's holiness was an important factor in his trouble. He had placed her on so high a pedestal that it would be impossible for any man to make love to her as long as she remained there. What was required was that she should descend from on high and I suggested to him, as tactfully as I could, that she might have womanly as well as saintly feelings, and advised him to be more outspoken with her concerning his sexual difficulties. He returned to me two months later and the situation had entirely changed. He and his wife had had a long talk together and the talk had ended in a terrible scene. He had discovered that his pure and too chaste bride had had a lover before marrying him and—what was much worse —she expressed no real regrets for what had happened. She fell with a crash from her pedestal, and although he had lost an ideal woman he gained in her stead something of far greater value to him, a warm-hearted and not over soulful wife. They are now both very happy.

Marriage entails the giving up of individual freedom but as little of this should be sacrificed as possible, for marriage should lead to a widening of horizons rather than to a narrowing of them.

> "Love one another, but make not a bond of loving,
>   Let it rather be a moving sea between the shores
>   of your souls,
>   Fill each other's cup but drink not from one cup.
>   Give one another of your bread, but eat not from
>   the same loaf.

Sing and dance together, but let each one of you
    be alone
Even as the strings of the lute are alone though
    they quiver with the same music.
Give your hearts but not into each other's keeping,
For only the hand of Life can contain your hearts.
And stand together, yet not too near together,
For the pillars of the temple stand apart
And the oak tree and the cypress grove are not
    in each other's shadow."

So wrote Kahlil Gibran in his poem *The Prophet*, and he gives us a much more satisfactory account of married life than that provided by R. L. Stevenson. The essence of married life is that it is a sharing and a giving rather than a taking. I sometimes picture a married couple as two people seated in a rather frail craft, which will require very skilful and careful handling if it is to ride safely through the many vicissitudes of weather and sea with which it is likely to meet in the course of their voyage. Some of the threats to the safety of the boat will arrive with startling suddenness, some will develop slowly, and a few will be seen looming on the horizon a long way off, so that evading action can be taken in plenty of time. At one moment the navigating couple are sailing in smooth water, at another they are being buffeted by a squall, and never for very long is the situation precisely the same. Now, however good the weather may be at the moment, and however confident they may be of the sea-worthiness of their craft, the more the couple know about the rocks and shoals which lie ahead of them, the better for them both. It is for the purpose of drawing attention to some of the dangers threatening the small boat of matrimony that this chapter has been written.

Money cannot buy love, nor can it sustain love which is sickening, but there can be no doubt that a grave shortage of money often throws a considerable strain on marriage. It provides a strong undercurrent of worry which is liable to sweep the craft of marriage out of its course in a dangerous direction. High taxation and the great rise in the cost of living have made money shortage a periodic problem, and a problem which should be the concern of both partners. The days are now gone in which the family finances were the responsibility only of the husband, and it is right that they should have gone. The wife should know when the bank account is in the red and be in a position to suggest what can be sacrificed in order to make ends meet. I speak here particularly of the middle classes on whom high taxation presses particularly heavily now owing to their not having received a compensatory rise in salaries. But what has been said applies also to a lesser extent to that section of society which was formerly known as the working classes. By making his wife his co-equal in financial affairs, the husband avoids the troubles which were formerly associated with her allowance and how she spent it. If the wife has a good money sense, or if she herself is contributing financially to the upkeep of the home, a joint banking account is often an excellent idea.

The great shortage of accommodation has meant that many young couples have had to start married life in the houses of their parents and this has been responsible for a great many marriage difficulties. There are few things more galling to a newly-wed husband and wife than to be compelled to share a house with somebody else, however kind and accommodating that somebody else may be. All the world over it is the custom of a husband to remove the girl on her wedding day from her parents' home and to present her with a new hut or house of her own, and the man who is unable to do what tradition decrees feels deeply humiliated. So also is it traditional for a newly-wed wife to take a special pride in her new home, and if she is living in rooms belonging to someone else she is robbed of this enjoyment. Neither the husband or wife are pleased with their substitute for a home of their own, and both are likely to become a trifle irritable about it. The situation is still more dangerous if the rooms they have been lent belong to the "in-laws". It is more dangerous because marriage should entail a clear break with the past, including the parents, and if the two young people have to live under the same roof as the "in-laws" the past remains with them, getting mixed up with the present. Not only is there a conflict of "times" for them but also a confusion of "rôles", the old rôle of the daughter clashing with the new one of the wife, and the old rôle of the son colliding with the new rôle of the husband. And this latter conflict between the rôles of son and husband is a specially dangerous one, for the mother-son relationship is a closer one than the father-daughter relationship. However glad a mother may say that she is about her son's marriage, subconsciously she often looks upon her daughter-in-law as an intruder. Previously she has had first place in her son's affections and now she is forced to give way to a woman who is much younger and more beautiful than herself. Subconsciously she may deeply resent this.

An additional complication sometimes exists which may render the situation still more difficult, the complication that the son has in fact never really broken away from his mother. He has married a wife but his mother still remains as his ideal of womanhood. Because of this he is apt to contrast the amateur efforts of his young and inexperienced wife with the cleverness and skill of his mother, and even though he does not say anything to his wife she may sense what is going on in his mind. Nor is this all that makes life difficult for the young wife. When the mother-son relationship has been a very close one, the mother is likely to be over-critical of everything her daughter-in-law does. All these psychological ingredients form a highly dangerous mixture, liable to explode at any minute.

Fathers-in-law are much less critical of their sons' wives and of their daughters' husbands than are mothers-in-law, but sisters-in-law are only a little less dangerous than mothers-in-law. They are dangerous for the very same reason, that they are over-critical of the young wives. "She's not nearly good enough for him", a sister remarks of a favourite brother's wife, and acting in accordance with this judgement she can be responsible for a great deal of harm. The above statements on the subject of the difficulties caused by the various "in-laws" are not merely the author's personal opinion but are statements based on statistics. But statistics allow of the existence of many exceptions and a mother-in-law can be an invaluable friend as well as an unmitigated nuisance to a young wife or husband.

If novelists are to be believed, the commonest cause of broken marriages is the intrusion of a third party. But actually the lover and the mistress are far more likely to appear in the last than in the first act of a marriage tragedy and to be a sign of the breakage rather than its cause. If all had been well with the home the lover or the mistress would have been unable to have gained an entry into it. It was only because the marriage was already in jeopardy that the third party was able to make a place for himself there, and to become that highly dangerous thing, a confidant.

Taking things for granted and taking each other for granted is another source of marital troubles. "He never seems to notice anything, even when I'm wearing a new frock or have had my hair done in a different way", a wife protests. "What is the good of doing anything in order to look nice if you are married to a man who doesn't see anything!" She is quite right, but that is the trouble with us all, that custom dulls our senses so that having seen a thing a hundred times we no longer notice it, however beautiful it be. What a thrill a sunset would impart to us if we were suddenly to come across it for the first time by accident on a country walk. But because we have seen so many sunsets we scarcely notice them. This may extenuate our guilt as husbands but it does not excuse it. Married people cannot afford to take each other for granted, as though they were of no greater significance than the dining-room chairs.

Balzac was a keen observer of married life and he wrote that it was much easier to be a lover than a husband, for whereas the former was only required to make an occasional pretty speech, the husband had to make one every day. British husbands should take a hint from this Frenchman, and even though they fail to attain so high a standard as a daily pretty speech to their wives, they should at least manage a weekly one. It will be deeply appreciated and will pay good dividends in the home. Nor need pretty speech-making necessarily be confined to the husband, for what is sauce for the goose is also sauce to the gander. The real trouble is that married people retire far too soon into a frowsy and graceless domesticity in which they are liable to take each other so much for granted that they scarcely notice one another's presence.

Familiarity is a breeder of contempt, and when regard for each other has disappeared in this way, the marriage is no longer a marriage but only a habit. Absence of respect and courtesy are ominous signs in a home, and if derogatory remarks are made in the presence of other people, the situation may be regarded as exceedingly bad. Sir Cyril Burt has recorded the complaints brought to him by disgruntled couples who would have preferred to have parted, had it been feasible for them to do so. The commonest complaint voiced by the husbands was that their wives were always "nagging" them, and the commonest complaint of the wives was that their husbands were entirely selfish and took no notice of them or of their children. These respective failings of the two sexes are so old that they have now become traditional. The feminine scold and the egotistical and brutal male are well-known characters in domestic history.

Habit is an arch enemy of marriage and it is astonishing how quickly it assumes charge of a home. But as R. L. Stevenson has pointed out, the material out of which many marriages are made is exceedingly poor, so far as the qualities of imagination and enterprise are concerned. Many people swallow the mysteries of their own existence with the same lack of wonder and concern as they swallow their morning cups of tea, so it is not in the least surprising that when they marry a humdrum atmosphere soon settles down on the home. Routine and convention soon rule there and if there were any tinge of romance in their marriage at the start of it that tinge soon disappears. Neither party takes much note of the other and when love-making occurs it is performed much as a person winds up a seven-day clock.

Wives are as often to blame for this as are their husbands. Indeed, their blame is usually greater for women are experts in personal relationship and if a marriage becomes dull and monotonous it is the result of a failure in the wife-husband relationship. There are, however, wives who are so ignorant of the psychology of men and of the refinements of love-making that they make no attempt to play the feminine rôle in this ancient art. They are under the impression that all that their husbands require of them is that they should submit to their embraces when asked to do so. "Always oblige your husband in the bedroom when it is necessary to do so", said a mother to her daughter on the eve of her marriage and it is in this spirit of "obliging" that many wives perform their marital duties. Women who adopt this attitude to love-making are mistaken and are also flattering their own charms unduly, for sexual intercourse is not a solo, that is to say a man performing on a woman, but a duet to which both should be making their appropriate contributions. In extreme youth little may be required of the female partner in love-making beyond submission, but as a man becomes older he also becomes more sexually exacting. It is not every woman who excites him now, but *this* woman or *that* woman only, and by the time that he has reached the forties or fifties he demands also that the setting should be propitious to his love-making. In allowing themselves to become shoddy and unattractive and in laying aside all the arts of their sex, such women are defrauding their husbands of what they need and imperilling the future of the marriage.

Sometimes this failure of wives to play the feminine rôle in marriage is due to an absurd mistake of theirs in the psychology of love and marriage. "If my husband really loves me", they say to themselves, "he will love me for *myself* and not for what I look like". No account of a man's psychology could be more grotesque than this. A wife can never afford to put aside her feminine arts however much her husband loves her and women who do this are taking immense risks. The correct advice for misguided wives of this sort is that they should go to the courtesan and learn wisdom from her, for the courtesan has undoubtedly acquired a form of wisdom in which they are singularly lacking—wisdom in the handling of men. Because a prostitute has a living to earn she usually goes to immense trouble in supplying what her customers require of her. She is an expert in the art of seduction, an artist in how to look, how to render herself pleasant to men, and even in how to disrobe. Nothing is so trivial that it is beneath her notice if it will add to the pleasure she is able to give her customers. It is ignominious of course that all this should be done for the sake of money only but many of these women are innately honest and they take a pride in giving full value for what they get. Women who despise the arts of the mistress and take no trouble with their appearance once they are married are less conscientious than they are.

I agree emphatically with those writers on marriage who assert, as Albert Moll does in the 1912 edition of his *Manual of Sexual Science*, that a strong link is established between a husband and a wife "when it is possible for the wife to stand shoulder to shoulder with her husband in his life-work, to be an adroit and efficient help-mate." He adds that this "is perhaps the reason why we find such comparatively happy marriages amongst small tradespeople, where the woman often helps by serving in the shop, or amongst artisans, where she often lends a hand with a job."

Marriages of this kind are also to be found amongst the more highly educated classes and no more striking example of one could possibly be cited than the marriage of the late Sidney and Beatrice Webb, afterwards Lord and Lady Passmoor. Never were complementary types more happily wedded together than in the case of this couple. Each supplied the qualities the other lacked, Beatrice confidence, initiative and drive, and Sidney industry and excellent judgement. Neither was able to go very far with any enterprise without the help of the other.

The lesson to be learnt from this couple is capable of being applied elsewhere. A clever and enterprising wife can help to avert that fatal *ennui* which so often settles down on homes after six or seven years of marriage, by encouraging her husband to take part with her in some outside interest. She can, for example, persuade him to share with her the reading aloud of some interesting book, to join in some small social or communal enterprise, to study music with her and attend occasional concerts, to make new friends, to go on what should prove to be an exceedingly interesting journey, to do a hundred small and novel things which, left to himself, he would never have contemplated.

All of these enterprises may be trifles, but in marriage they may become of tremendous importance. Even hobbies as banal as a joint collection of postage stamps, the doing of crossword or chess puzzles together, or work together in the garden can act as a bulwark against that most insidious of foes—marriage boredom. Children are, of course, the best possible form of joint enterprise for married people, but in their absence something else will have to be found. All that is required is an activity which appeals to both of them with an approximately equal force. Preferably it should also be an enterprise which demands of both of them a certain amount of initiative.

There are critical periods in married life, stages of the joint journey when upsets are particularly likely to occur. One of these periods comes at the beginning of marriage when a satisfactory sexual adjustment has not yet been attained, and these early difficulties have been dealt with at some length in Chapters Eight and Nine. Another awkward period calling for fresh adjustments is likely to occur when the family arrives. Hitherto the husband has had first place in his wife's affections but now he is faced with a rival in the shape of the family and without in the least realizing this he may deeply resent the intrusion of this new claimant on his wife's love. There are other periods in married life which may cause temporary difficulties to both parties. The first is when the sexual links have weakened, in the course of years, and in most successful of marriages this is bound to happen. But by the time that this weakening occurs the other ingredients of the composite love which holds the husband and wife together should have grown stronger, so that the necessary readjustments can easily be made. The final critical period during which all the little difficulties associated with married life are likely to increase is at the time of the female menopause or change of life.

This critical period marks the end of a woman's reproductive life and it can occur anywhere between the ages of forty-five and fifty. It is associated with irregularity and finally with cessation of the menstrual flow, with involutionary changes in the reproductive organs and often with a temporary upset in the balance of the endocrine or ductless glands. The last named may lead to such psychological disturbances as moodiness, irritability and depression. Difficulties between husband and wife which formerly were easily dispelled are now liable to last longer and to provoke more irritation. Because of all this the attitude of both partners to this critical period in their married life is of the greatest importance. A happily married couple who have attained a high level of mutual understanding will get through this troublesome time without much difficulty, but a less well adjusted pair are likely to find it exceedingly trying. Husbands can do a great deal to help their wives during this season of physical and psychological discomforts by making allowances for their irritability, just as they formerly made allowances for their irritability before the onset of the menstrual flow. A woman who is secure in her husband's love and understanding will get through the change of life with far less distress to herself than a woman who cannot count on either of these. Her purely physical discomforts, such as her hot flushes, can also be alleviated by taking the appropriate endocrine remedies.

Motorists are given books of instructions, with such titles as "Rules of the Road" and "Hints to Motorists", and if I were to be asked to write a similar guide for those who are driving down the highway of matrimony, I should include in it the following maxims:

1. Don't try to reform your partner, but keep all your reforming zeal for yourself.
2. Cultivate mutual trust and kill every suspicion in its infancy.
3. Don't minimize the importance of small things in married life.
4. Don't become slovenly in dress, however uninterested you may be in your own appearance.

5. Let there be plenty of give and take, but no form of book-keeping in your relationship.
6. Never brood on a grievance alone but bring it out for discussion with your partner, a friendly discussion if possible.
7. Remember that you are both engaged on the same task of creating what never comes by itself—a successful marriage.
8. Respect the rights and privileges of your partner.
9. Do your best to remember anniversaries and don't forget the importance to a woman of unexpected and unnecessary presents.
10. Never remind your partner of a past mistake, and apologize for what may seem to you to be only a trifling error.
11. Never both be angry at the same moment and only shout if the house be on fire.
12. Never refer slightingly to your husband or your wife when in company.
13. Remember that you and your partner are both human beings with all the imperfections and weaknesses which this entails. Confucianism or the cult of the "superior person" no longer exists, even in the land of its origin—China.

(I am indebted to my friend, Sir Adolphe Abrahams, for some of the above matrimonial maxims.)

17

THE EXPECTANT FATHER

THAT men should know more about the mysteries of pregnancy and childbirth became apparent to me nearly thirty years ago, in the Gray's Inn Road where a coffee stall offered its hospitality to wayfarers. I happened to stop at it on my way back from the Royal Free Hospital. Two men were there drinking their coffee and munching their ham sandwiches. Now although they seemed to be strangers to each other and came from different social levels, they had this in common, that they drank and they ate with an air of intense preoccupation, as though their minds were concerned with very grave matters. At last one of them broke the silence with a commonplace remark which led on to others, and eventually to the discovery that they were both in the same predicament. They were on the eve of domestic events of serious import, and before the sun ushered in another day they might both be fathers. The discovery drew the two men together and led to an exchange of confidences. The wife of one was expecting the arrival of her doctor in an hour's time, whilst the other had just said good-bye to his wife at the Royal Free Hospital where she was to have her confinement. Both men had stepped out for a breath of fresh air before returning to await the imminent event with whatever patience they could summon. Their anxiety—and they were both exceedingly scared—was due to their complete ignorance of what was about to happen to their wives, and their inability to find anyone who would enlighten them.

Why are men kept in the dark at such times and why cannot they be told something about what is happening? There are hundreds of books written for mothers and expectant mothers, but not even a tract for fathers and expectant fathers. I had arrived at the coffee stall in time to hear the conversation of these deeply disturbed husbands and decided that something must be done about it. I would persuade some gynaecological colleague of mine to divert his attention for a moment or two from the over-pampered expectant mother and give it to the totally neglected expectant father.

Dr. Marie Stopes had just published a book entitled *Radiant Motherhood*, so why should not a companion volume be brought out under the title of *Radiant Fatherhood*? No, that would be overdoing things, for all that was required of the expectant father was that he should be less harassed and more helpful, not that he should be radiant. But in spite of my appeals, none of my gynæcological colleagues would undertake the task I had allotted to him. In consequence of this I was forced to do it myself and much of the material used in the present chapter has been taken from that old work of mine, *On Being a Father*.

First let us try to determine the rôle of the father by seeing what happens in the animal world. The part played by the male in the care of offspring differs very widely in different species of animals. The insect father, for example, takes his parental duties very lightly so long as he lives, and this may not be for very long, for in the communistic world of the bee the fate of the father is a tragic one. Having proved a winner against many male competitors in the nuptial flight and carried out his work of fertilizing the queen bee satisfactorily, he is of no further use to the hive and is expelled to die outside of cold and starvation. The treatment of spider fathers is still more heartless. Having carried out his work, he is promptly dispatched by his wife, who has no further interest in him as a lover.

In the fish world customs are exceedingly varied and in some species the father actually spends more time guarding the eggs than does the mother fish. Some expectant fish fathers are provided with special pouches in which the eggs are carried until hatched, and a similar arrangement is found in certain varieties of frog. The male frog's pouch lies under his throat, and the eggs are deposited in it. There they increase in size and "spread along the skin of the belly until the whole under-surface of the belly is full of them." (W. P. Pyecroft: *Infancy of Animals*). Few human fathers would tolerate such an inconvenient method of replenishing their nurseries.

When we reach the level of the mammals we find that the bond between the offspring and their mother is greatly strengthened, whilst the link between the offspring and their father is correspondingly weakened. The explanation of this change in the maternal and paternal rôles is that in mammals the care and development of the fertilized egg has become the responsibility of the mother's body, thereby relieving the mammal father of the duties which are carried out by fathers in lowlier walks of the animal world. This leads to a weakening of the paternal instinct and to the restriction of the male's function to protecting the female and her offspring from attack. The males of gregarious animals are quite prepared to carry out this paternal duty when an attack is unavoidable but they much prefer to take refuge in flight whenever this alternative is offered them. Their attitudes to the does and to the young is that of owners rather than that of affectionate husbands and fathers, and Dr. Chalmers Mitchell states that he has never known a mammal male show any real affection for his offspring. "Generally they neglect them altogether or attack them and persecute them." But what the mammal father has lost, the mother has gained, and it is in the female mammal that the maternal instinct reaches its highest development.

In other words, in the animal world the paternal instinct is weak in comparison with the maternal instinct and this is true of human fathers also. Few men would undertake the countless services rendered to an infant by its mother, and still fewer would volunteer for the more tedious and exacting work of nurturing the developing child and bringing it into the world. So also would I consider it true to say that if the care of the older children were to be left in the hands of the fathers, many of them would grow up underfed, dirty, ill-mannered and unkempt. It is fortunate indeed that amongst human beings, as amongst animals, the duties of the father are restricted. Not that the human father should be or wants to be exempted from all duties, anxieties and responsibilities, either during his wife's pregnancy or subsequently. Experience shows that he suffers many discomforts and worries at such times and it is for the purpose of dealing with these paternal difficulties and of showing him how a husband can help his over-burdened wife, that the present chapter is written.

Pregnancy is often associated with marked psychological changes in a woman, changes which are sometimes so puzzling and unexpected that they may disturb her husband greatly. In women of an hysterical temperament these emotional and functional upsets may be so striking as to cause him considerable anxiety, and even in well-balanced, easy-going women they are often very perplexing to the male. They manifest themselves in many ways, such as in a great intensification of likes and dislikes of every kind and frequently also in a sudden craving for unusual kinds of food. For example, a pregnant woman may develop an unaccountable longing for shrimps or for fruit which happens to be out of season at that particular time. Or she may have a sudden desire for food which is regarded by everybody else as being highly indigestible and unsuitable to a person in her condition. But it is best, whenever this is possible, to satisfy her longings without being too concerned as to whether it is suitable for a pregnant woman or not. The woman's body often knows what is required better than another person's mind, even the trained mind of the doctor. But the alteration in the expectant mother's likes and dislikes may affect things far more nearly related to the husband than food and drink. Pregnancy may, for the time being, change her attitude to her husband and express itself either in an increased desire for his company or else in a strong aversion to it. In her mind her husband is closely linked with the fact that she is now pregnant, and when pregnancy happens to be unwelcome to her, some of her resentment against her lot is liable to spill over on to him. A husband who does not understand the reason for this abrupt change in his wife's feelings for him may make things worse by arguing with her and trying to overcome her irrational prejudice. What it would be much wiser for him to do would be to help her in every possible way he can and show her all the forbearance, patience, love and understanding that lie within his power. Her behaviour is emotional and perhaps even physiological in its origin and argument is not only useless but likely to aggravate the condition.

It is a law that whenever the physical differences between the two sexes become accentuated, as happens during the woman's periods and whilst she is pregnant, the psychological characteristics of the two sexes also become more marked. This is not in the least surprising when we remember that the woman's tissues are flooded at such times with female hormones. Nothing is better calculated to bring out these sexual differences than the starting of some trivial argument by the husband or the wife. In characteristic male fashion the husband strives to convert his wife to his own way of thinking by means of a well constructed chain of argument, in the expectation that if he can get her to see the situation as it actually is and as *he* sees it, she will immediately capitulate. But to the wife his well-reasoned arguments are entirely useless. For her they are only the wordy puppets with which men amuse themselves when they have grown too old to play any more with their old lead soldiers. She knew from the very start that she is right, so why all these absurd arguments of her husband's? Will he never learn that a woman has other ways of reaching truth than those employed by a man? And sometimes it happens that the wife is right and not the husband. In any case they are moving on entirely different planes, the wife on the emotional plane and the husband on the intellectual plane and for him to attempt to overcome her intuition by means of his logic is a vain beating of the air.

Was it the unassailable unreasonableness and pig-headedness of pregnant women which gave rise to the primitive belief that when a woman was with child she was particularly open to possession by a demon? This is certainly a very widespread belief and special precautions are taken by many tribes to protect expectant mothers from possession. In the Celebes no woman with child is ever allowed to walk about unattended, especially if her hair is unbraided, for it is in loose hair that predatory demons are likely to hide.

A similar belief existed formerly in the country parts of Czechoslovakia and Esthonia, and in the latter country a clever ruse was employed to mislead prowling demons. It was for all pregnant women to change their shoes very often with the idea that the demon who followed their tracks would thereby be thrown into confusion. But whether the expectant mother resorts to magic, or whether she pins her faith to the latest concoctions of the manufacturing chemist, the result is much the same; she seldom manages to escape from emotional confusion and sudden changes of mood. For no apparent cause at all she will dissolve into tears, and with an equal lack of reason she will quickly recover her spirits and be all smiles and laughter again.

Her sorely puzzled husband looks on, not knowing what to do about it. But the remedy for it all is really a very simple one—she wants him to be particularly nice to her and a kiss will do more than any medicine.

Another trouble is added during the later months of her pregnancy, and one which her husband finds it equally difficult to understand. She becomes more and more distressed about the change in her figure and is as sensitive concerning it in the privacy of her home as she is when she is abroad amongst strangers. That a woman should take so natural a change in her figure so seriously astonishes some husbands, but it is very easily explained. A woman's capacity to charm is perhaps the most valuable of all her assets. It was by means of this power of hers that she won her husband and it is with its help that she will retain him. Small wonder therefore that she looks upon her present disfigurement as harder to bear than her physical discomforts. Just at the time when she needs it most, she is deprived of the reassurance which comes to a woman from the knowledge that she is looking her best. The shapeless gown of the matron is utterly abhorrent to her and she hates the smart women who look at her critically as she passes them in the street. To look nice is instinctive in her and she may become so over-sensitive about her appearance towards the end of pregnancy that she will take her walks only under cover of darkness.

All women do not suffer in this way. Some accept the change in their appearance quite calmly if they have borne children previously. So also are there women who are exceptionally well during the whole of their pregnancy. But the demands made on the organism by pregnancy are always very heavy, for not only has the body to provide for the growth and nourishment of the developing child, but it has to do all this at a time when some of its organs are working under difficulties, as, for example, when the expectant mother is suffering from severe morning sickness. During the later months, going upstairs, which at ordinary times is almost effortless, may become a real ordeal. The cares and preoccupations of housekeeping have also to be carried on, and quite possibly there are other children in the house to be looked after. All these things throw a strain on the expectant mother and she is in need of all the help her husband can give her.

A husband may have some emotional difficulties of his own to deal with during his wife's pregnancy, and the fact that there is not a great deal he can do to ease the situation in the house tends to accentuate them. It is quite common for expectant fathers to experience occasional pangs of jealousy and hostility towards the coming child. Even though it is still in the womb, it is taking a great deal of its mother's energy and time, and, without being fully aware of the reason, husbands may resent this. It is not uncommon for them to develop all sorts of unusual aches and pains, without realizing that this is an attempt on the part of the less conscious layers of their mind to recapture some of their wives' attention. If a husband can catch sight of himself in the act of manifesting jealousy for the unborn babe, he will perhaps be able to laugh at his own foolishness and thus deprive the jealousy of much of its power over him.

Psychologists tell us that sometimes expectant fathers develop a feeling of guilt on the score of their wives' pregnancy, and that this guilt is usually the result of early training. As young men they had to listen to stern harangues from their own fathers about the need for controlling their sexual desires for fear of "getting some girl into trouble", and this feeling has been carried over into marriage. No matter how much they may desire children, on the conscious levels of their minds, they may feel guilty about their wives' pregnancy on the unconscious levels. What has for so long been representative in their minds of "being all wrong" has not yet been converted into "being all right". This guilty feeling may show itself in different ways and often as an exaggerated solicitude for their wives' safety. Fearing that they have endangered their wives' lives by making them pregnant, they encourage their wives to become hypochondriacal over their health.

What a husband has to try to do is to steer between the extremes of being too fussy about his wife's health, thus rendering her also too concerned about it, and appearing to be indifferent to her various aches and pains. He should start by accepting the normality of the pregnancy and childbirth processes, and he should encourage her to do the same. But as time goes on she will probably require his help over certain of the household jobs which she has previously been able to do alone, and it is by being always on the look-out for occasions on which she needs his help and by the promptness with which he offers it that he will be able to show his solicitude for her welfare.

Guidance is often sought on the subject of sexual intercourse during pregnancy. There is a certain risk attached to vigorous love-making during the first two months, namely, the risk of provoking a miscarriage and, this being so, intercourse should be gentle and perhaps less frequent than usual. If a miscarriage has happened previously, it is better to avoid it altogether during this period. In the later months, when the risk of miscarriage has become much less, it can be resumed and continued, if desired, until physical changes render it too difficult. A period of two months' abstinence has to be observed after the child has been born.

In former years a certain diagnosis of pregnancy could never be guaranteed during the first few weeks, but now, thanks to the Aschein-Zondek test, pregnancy can be detected after the first few days. All that is required for this test to be carried out is that a small bottle of the urine passed first thing in the morning should be sent to the laboratory for examination. If pregnancy has occurred the urine is full of pituitary-like hormones, and when a small quantity of it is injected into a young female rabbit, toad or mouse, it produces immediate activity and growth of the ovaries. The test is of great value and through it the many mistakes which were formerly made in the diagnosis of pregnancy are avoided. Errors of this kind were particularly likely to be made in the case of an hysterical woman who has a very strong desire to become a mother, for such a woman has the power to evoke in herself many of the physical changes associated with pregnancy, such as a cessation of the periods, enlargement of the breasts and morning vomiting. Many of these errors in diagnosis are corrected later but some of them go on to full term and end in a spurious labour. Occasionally these spurious pregnancies and labours are the result of the opposite state of mind, namely of an intense fear of child-bearing.

As pregnancy advances new questions arise for the couple, the most important being the problem of the confinement and where it shall take place. Formerly the great majority of women preferred to be confined in their own homes, but nowadays with the great difficulty of obtaining domestic help, and with the facilities given by the new Health Act, confinements in hospitals and nursing homes are becoming much more popular. From the medical point of view a hospital is much to be preferred, especially in first confinements. However well the patient has supported her pregnancy, and however satisfactory her condition is at the moment, a complication may arise during labour which can be much more satisfactorily dealt with in a hospital or properly equipped nursing home. It is always wiser, therefore, to be prepared for such emergencies, however unlikely they may be.

It is also important that the expectant mother should be under the care of the doctor who is to confine her, from the very

ritual is practised, the expectant father's responsibilities start quite early in pregnancy when he is forced to regulate his diet very carefully. He has to give up taking certain foods entirely and for very definite reasons. If, for example, he were to continue eating "water haas" his child would be born with the protruding tusks possessed by that animal. So also if he were to eat the "spotted labba", a baby would be born with similar spotty markings.

In Guiana the paternal anti-natal régime is even stricter. Sir Everard Thurn tells us that it is believed that if the expectant father were to eat strong food, were to wash, smoke or handle weapons, then it would have precisely the same result as if the babe were to carry out these actions also (Sir Everard Thurn *Amongst the Indians of Guiana*). In order to prevent this, the expectant father must do without his curry, must lay aside his pipe and must await with patience the start of *his own* labour pains; yes, his own labour pains. With the onset of these pains the more critical part of the Couvade begins. Meanwhile the wife, who has continued living a normal life and working up to the onset of her own labour pains, retires quietly into the forest with some of her women friends and there she bears her child without any fuss. As she suffers very little, she is soon back at work again. Not so her poor husband. As soon as news reaches him of the birth of the child he takes to his bed, eats no meat and abstains from all other forms of food, except perhaps a little thin cassava juice. He also continues to avoid washing, smoking and contact with any weapon and so strict is he about this that should he have to scratch himself he avoids using his own fingernail for this purpose but uses instead a small splinter of coconut palm. His confinement lasts for several days or even for several weeks, and during the whole of this time he is looked after and ordered about by the women midwives of the village.

How has this elaborate ritual come into existence and is there any link between a husband and a wife at these times, a sympathy of a stronger and more compelling nature than the ordinary emotions of affection? There are those who believe that some mysterious link of this kind exists. Monthly nurses tell stories of husbands who are so strongly affected by what is happening to their wives that they suffer from similar bouts of sickness and pains. I cannot vouch for the accuracy of the following story, told me at first hand. The narrator described how he was attending a luncheon party at the Adelphi Hotel, Liverpool, at about the time that his wife was expecting to be confined. Soon after seating himself at the luncheon table he was seized with abdominal pain so violent in character that he was forced to withdraw hurriedly to avoid vomiting in the presence of a smart gathering. He came back to the table a little later, but to his surprise and annoyance the same symptoms recurred, so that he was forced to retire again. As he had not eaten anything at all he was at a loss to explain his seizure, but on getting back to his office he found a telephone message awaiting him there to the effect that his wife had just been delivered of a child after a very rapid and violent labour. He maintains that his pains synchronized with those of his wife, and no longer looks upon the idea of the Couvade as being ridiculous.

Labour is due to start in the pregnant woman about two hundred and seventy eight days after the termination of her last period, but babies are not necessarily punctual in their appearance, more especially first babies. The mechanism which starts the labour is not yet fully known, but the hormones or secretions of the ductless glands certainly have a great deal to do with it. All that can be said about the onset of labour is that after a period of comparative quiescence, muscular contractions begin in the womb. These contractions are entirely automatic, that is to say not under the control of the will, although they are influenced by the emotions. Warning that labour has actually started is given by the contractions becoming much more frequent and more regular and also by the appearance of what is known as "a show", the escape of a small amount of blood-stained mucus. This is a sign that the jelly-like secretion which up till now has plugged the cervical canal has been expelled.

Labour is divisible into three stages: the first stage is occupied with the dilation of the cervex, or neck of the womb; the second with the descent and the delivery of the child, and the third with the expulsion of the placenta or "after-birth." The time taken for the completion of these various stages varies greatly in different women and is of course much shorter when a woman has borne a child before. Reckoning from the onset of the first regular and true labour pains, the average duration of the labour is about fifteen hours, for first labours, and eight hours for subsequent confinements. At least three-quarters of this time is taken up by the first stage of labour, that is to say by the dilating of the cervex. The age of the mother also affects the time taken for this dilation. When she is over thirty-four and it is her first child, the tissues are less easily stretched than are the tissues of a woman still in the twenties, and this is one of the reasons why some gynaecologists prefer to deliver a woman having her first baby in the late thirties or early forties by means of Caesarian section.

The above figures for the total duration of labour are taken from an analysis of a large number of uncomplicated births, but it is quite common for the delivery to be temporarily delayed by a falling off in the strength of the labour pains. Sometimes this is due to fatigue of the mother and sometimes it is the result of narcotics given to her in order to relieve pain. Whatever the explanation, there is no cause for alarm, for sooner or later stronger contractions of the uterus will be resumed.

At the beginning of the century, it was fashionable to give women in labour various opium derivatives in order to diminish pain and to induce in them the state known as "twilight sleep." This practice has become much less common and patients are now taught how to relax their muscles and thus help the mechanism of expulsion. Relaxation methods of delivery entail no risk at all to the child, whereas the giving of opium derivatives was associated with a small risk.

In the rush of telephoning to relations and friends about the safe arrival of a child, and of sending an announcement of the birth off to the papers, the father is liable to forget that the birth has also to be registered at the office of the Registrar of Births and Deaths. Only then is the poor but no longer expectant father able to retire to his den, light his pipe, lean far back in his chair, heave a sigh of intense relief, and ponder over his new responsibilities. His responsibilities will start very soon, or it would be more accurate to say that they have already begun.

According to the psychologists, a new-born baby is more aware of what is happening to himself than the adults around him realize. He has been considerably upset by his tempestuous passage into this noisy world, and is already looking back with longing at the cosy and quiet world of the womb from which he has been so recently expelled. This being so, he is depressed in spirit and in need of assurance and comfort. Dr. Spurgeon English tells us that many patients suffering from various forms of neurosis reveal under psycho-analysis a deeply unsatisfied longing for the comfort and irresponsibility of pre-natal existence. It is well worth remembering that some of the anxieties and tensions of later life may be due to the rather impersonal treatment of the new-born after the hospital delivery. In short, the newly arrived child is much in need of comfort and a warm welcome to cushion the shock of his abrupt arrival.

Our civilization has too long been unaware of the infant's needs in this matter of being born, tending to regard him almost as an inanimate object, too new and unformed to have any feelings. "Mother gets an anæsthetic to ease her pain; father gets a drink, perhaps, to relax his tension; the obstetrician gets paid for his time and skill. But all the baby gets is a quick look to see if he's a boy or a girl, a slap on the buttocks, a dangling by the feet, a sharp dose of painful eye-drops, the discomfort of being enclosed in garments for the first time, and then lonely isolation in a sterile nursery where busy nurses have no time to pay attention to his cries—no doubt for the life he has left behind". (*Fathers are Parents Too*, by English and Foster, 1953. Allen & Unwin).

The sooner, therefore, that the father gets out of his easy chair and goes into the room where his son is lying, to welcome him to this new world, the better. A long speech will be unnecessary. All that is required is a friendly nod, a smile, the pat of a finger on the cheek, perhaps, and then a quiet withdrawal. In this simple manner begins, let us hope, a long and very successful father-son or father-daughter relationship.

It has to be admitted that during the last century the father figure in the home has been steadily shrinking, so that in many households it is only a third of the size it formerly was. As Dr. English and Mrs. Foster have put it: "In the days when a man shaved with a straight razor, drank his coffee out of a moustache cup with "Father" emblazoned on it in gold letters, and administered the strap to a recalcitrant offspring, no one questioned his position as head of the family. His home was his stronghold. His children were supposed to be seen but not heard. When he was angry the house shook, his wife trembled, and his offspring quaked in their high buttoned boots. He earned the living and held the purse strongs. His word was Law. And he issued many more than ten commandments."

But those Jovian days are now over and the patriarchal "father" has undergone a series of changes, giving place first to "papa", then to "daddy", next to "dad", and finally to "the old man". More often than not, and especially in the United States, the nominal head of the family has become a tired business man lurking somewhere in the background and so occupied with earning sufficient money to support his wife and family that he is unable to see much of any of them. The centre of power in the family and its chief executive office is no longer invested in the father but has been transferred to the mother. It is to their mother that the children look up and to her that they always go for advice when in trouble. The father has become too uncertain a figure to be of practical use. He only appears occasionally and is too erratic for them to be able to count on him.

Now no one wants the heavy-handed and despotic male head of the family back again, but there can be no doubt at all that the father has a very important part to play in the psychological development of the children, and that the child of today often suffers from his absence. It is high time, therefore, that this third member of the triad father-mother-child resumed his paternal duties. Psychologists tell us that on account of his absence many boys are growing up into hesitant, truculent, vacillating and irresponsible youths, and that the effect of the absence of a father on the daughters' lives is to render them insecure, emotionally unstable, contemptuous of men, "or else too painfully eager to please them, unrealistic about romance, disinterested in home-making, undecided about marriage, doubtful of their own worth, moody and unmotivated". (*Fathers are Parents Also*. English & Foster).

We must agree, therefore, that the father is a necessary figure in the home and that his duties cannot all be delegated to the mother, as is the tendency at the present time. It is from the father that the family should derive a feeling of steadiness of purpose, a sense of security, an idea of justice and fair play, and a knowledge of their relationship with the great, noisy, booming world outside the home circle. The mother has other functions to perform. So let him return to his vacant seat at the head of the table, carve the joint on Sunday—when the family is sufficiently well off to buy a joint—maintain peace between warring elements in the family, serve as an example to his growing sons, give his daughter experience in dealing with men, and genuinely maintain the tradition and the good humour of the family.

18

SEX IN CHILDHOOD AND ADOLESCENCE

In the early decades of the present century Freud's writings provoked a good deal of acrimonious discussion, and none was more heated than that which centred around the subject of sexuality in the child. Hitherto it had been believed that the child spent his early years in a garden of innocence, exempt from all sexual impulses, and that if these were to manifest themselves they would have to be regarded as being grossly perverse. But Freud's theory of the *libido* denied this idea of childish innocence, and so strong was his influence on thought at that time that all sorts of seemingly innocent actions, such as sucking the thumb, became invested with sexual significance. The idea of an age of innocence was abandoned, and even so natural an emotion as the love of an infant for its mother was now looked upon with suspicion. Sexuality was said to be rampant both in the nursery and the schoolroom, and sexual significance was discovered in everything a child did. What truth lay in all this?

We have no direct access to an infant's mind and can only watch its behaviour and draw our conclusions from what we see. For the infant the earliest years of life are devoted to a never-ending investigation of the world around him and of his relationship to that equally strange world which lies within himself. At first there seems to be very little difference between these two worlds, and it is all very confusing for him. The infant grasps his foot, conveys it to his mouth, bites it, and is promptly informed by pain that the thing he has discovered and is now trying to eat is not something like his feeding bottle but a veritable part of himself. The division between the "me" and the "not-me" is slowly made.

During these formative years of discovering by means of trial and error what lies within and what lies without, the infant's curiosity is boundless. He is indeed the most tenacious and the most single-minded of all researchers. Everything has to be handled, investigated, and if possible pulled apart, and to the adults around him this behaviour of his is often highly disconcerting and even alarming. From the child's point of view it is entirely natural, and amongst the many things to be explored are his own genitalia and excreta. Infantile behaviour of this kind is a necessary step to his finding an adjustment to the environment, and if any other motive has to be found for it, that motive is far more likely to be self-assertion than sexuality. Biology supports this non-sexual view of the infant's behaviour, for the genitalia are so rudimentary in both sexes at this time that they are quite incapable of fulfilling any sexual function or of giving any sexual pleasure.

Much of the confusion caused by Freud's teaching about sexuality in infancy would have been avoided if he had chosen a word other than *libido* for the life force. Libido suggests the adjective "libidinous", a word which is very closely linked with sexuality, and Freud was later driven to explain that his term *libido* included much more than sexual desire. But the public still continued to use it in its narrower sense, and it would have been better if he had got rid of it altogether and had employed instead Jung's term "psychic energy", or the still broader term used by Bergson, "elan vital". Had he done this, further confusion would have been avoided. People would have ceased to regard an infant's preoccupation with his own genital organs as a sexual manifestation and would have looked upon it instead as an example of the pleasure-pain principle which determines so much in both animal and human behaviour.

The term pleasure-pain principle means nothing more than that a child behaves as though its sole guide to living is to find and to enjoy bodily sensation, and to avoid everything that is frustrating or painful in nature. Thus he extracts sensual enjoyment from such bodily activities as sucking, defæcating, passing urine, having his skin stimulated, and even from displaying his nakedness. At that tender age these activities are sensual only and are devoid of all sexual elements. It is quite true that at puberty they acquire a sexual significance, but in the infant they have not yet attained this meaning.

Present-day psychologists are steadily moving away from the old Freudian standpoints, and instead of interpreting childish behaviour in terms of sexuality they are describing it in terms of the child's efforts to find a relationship with other people and with his immediate environment. It must be borne in mind that the infant is almost entirely dependent for any feeling of security upon his parents' gestures of affection, and as yet he is unable to discriminate between what his parents intend to do and what they actually do. He is therefore puzzled and disconcerted by any alterations of mood such as when the mother he loves becomes irritable with him or treats him with indifference, and he is swept down by this change from the heights of enjoyment into the abysses of despair. The memories of childhood can be revised by the process known as psycho-analysis, and the fact that they are often found to be heavily charged with emotion, with intense love, hatred, jealousy, anger or fear, is beyond dispute. So also is it certain that the emotional shocks and crises of childhood may have disastrous consequences, not only for their victim's subsequent sex life but also for his non-sexual relationship with other people. It is not the emphasis placed by Freud on these early events which is in any doubt, but his method of interpreting them. Havelock Ellis has summarized my own feelings on this subject in the following paragraphs: "Children are at work—or, if you wish, at play—in the exercise ground of inquisitive reason and as yet un-differentiated emotion. Until we have realized this, until we have cleared away the elaborate structure of childhood sexu-ality, erected on the adult pattern by adults who seem to have lost all memory of youth, we shall wander among vain shadows in this field. Here certainly is a kingdom of knowledge into which only those can enter who become as little children". (Havelock Ellis, *The Psychology of Sex*. Heinemann).

It is a mistake, therefore, for anyone to be horrified when a child shows interest in his own genitalia or even when at a later age he discovers that by handling these organs in a certain way he can obtain sensual pleasure. So also is it an error to conclude, as some parents do, that when a child has acquired this habit he has necessarily learnt it from somebody else. André Gide recalls his own earliest sensuous experiences in *Si le grain ne meurt* and describes how as a little boy he used to play with the porter's small son beneath the nursery table. " 'What are you doing down there' cried my nurse. 'Nothing. We're just playing.' "And we noisily tossed about some toys we had taken with us so as to pretend to play with them. In fact, we were amusing ourselves in a different way, close to each other but not with one another. We had, as I learned later on, what are called 'bad habits'. Which of us taught the other? Who had taught the first of us? I do not know. One must admit that sometimes a child invents such things alone. As far as I am concerned I can-not say whether anybody ever taught me, or how I discovered the pleasure: but as far as I can remember it has always been there."

The adult's attitude to such infantile events as these is often singularly stupid, and may have very serious consequences for the child. In the past it was a common practice to try to stop such habits by means of implanting in the child both guilt and fear. He was told that terrible consequences would result from the persistence of such evil habits, and a rich harvest of sexual neuroses has been reaped from this unforgivable method of treatment. I have had to deal with men in the fifties who were still suffering from the guilt which had been instilled into them at the tender age of eight. It is interesting to note that many of the parents, teachers, and clergy who used this abominable method of treatment were themselves the victims of repressed feelings of guilt acquired at the time of their own past infantile indulgences.

Masturbation should be regarded, as other childish games have to be regarded, as being quite natural dress-rehearsals for what is to happen later on, in adult life. At the same time, masturbation may have an additional significance of practical importance. It may be an indication that the child in question has an unsatisfying life, lacking in richness and that he is in need of help. It is the lonely and emotionally dissatisfied child, possessed of few other interests, who is most likely to have recourse to this solitary method of obtaining pleasure and the correct treatment, therefore, is to provide the child with companions and with as many competitive interests as possible. It is also advisable to be quite open and honest with a child concerning what he or she is doing. Instead of pretending that it has not been noticed, the parent, or the adult in charge of the child, should speak to him quietly and in as detached a manner as possible. He should be told that it is better for him at present to indulge in what he has been doing as little as possible, but nothing should be added to this advice which would undermine his confidence in himself or make him feel guilty, or suggest that he is in any way lacking in will-power. Only if the child gives evidence of such neurotic symtoms as depression, nightmares, outbursts of temper, or excessive shyness, need psychological advice be sought.

What has been said about the treatment of solitary masturbation in childhood can also be said, with slight additions, about mutual masturbation later on. It has already been said that interest in and desire for a member of the same sex can be regarded as a natural and passing phase in the journey towards sexual maturity, a phase which many people are able to recall. It is a grave mistake, therefore, to regard it with the aversion and horror with which it has been regarded in the past. For example, it is absurd and even cruel to put a lasting stigma on a boy by expelling him from school for such a fault. Discipline, of course, has to be maintained in the school, but some other means can be devised to render undesirable practices of this kind unpopular in the school, and to protect smaller boys from being seduced by older ones. The weaning of a child from a habit based on the pleasure-pain principle—and mutual masturbation is a habit learnt in this way—must be done firmly but without overloading the offender with a burden of guilt which he may have to carry with him, in his subconscious mind, for the rest of his life.

Between infancy and puberty there is a quiescent interval of several years during which sexuality sinks into the background of the child's mind, so that he is no longer preoccupied with his own genitalia and—should he have acquired that habit—ceases to masturbate. This is a period of extraordinarily rapid physical growth and of still more rapid mental development. Up till now the whole of the child's emotional needs have been centred on his mother and satisfied by his mother, but at about the age of five a change is noted in this mother-child relationship. Although the support and influence of his mother is still pre-eminent in the child's life he becomes capable of forming relationships with other people as well. His relationship with his father is particularly likely to grow in importance about this time and he may even succeed in establishing ties with individuals completely outside the family circle. The normal healthy child of this age is by nature eager to make friends even with strangers and he accepts them at sight, provided that the parents themselves are positive and responsive in their attitude to those they meet. For the child is essentially an imitator and he responds much more readily to what his parents *do* than to what they merely *say*.

It is during these formative years that the psychological climate of the home has such a powerful effect on the growing and extremely plastic child. Dr. Stafford Clark writes of this sensitivity and responsiveness of children to the home atmosphere as follows: "They reflect with uncanny fidelity the moods and preoccupations and tensions of those nearest and dearest to them, often without realizing or understanding anything about these moods and tensions at all. But no matter how severe may be the impact upon a child of unhappiness, resentment or insecurity in his parents, it is nearly always possible for that child to regain an emotional equilibrium within normal limits, if the parental trouble can be removed or relieved. This is one of the most important discoveries of the branch of psychiatry known as child guidance". (Dr. Stafford Clark, *Psychiatry Today*, 1955. Pelican).

With the dawn of adolescence this period of freedom from sexuality comes to an end and sexuality again asserts itself. Emotional fulfilment can no longer be satisfied by the child's relationship with the parents and he looks farther afield for his needs, first to members of his own sex and then to members of the opposite sex. This final turning to members of the opposite sex can be regarded as the culmination of the individual's sexual pilgrimage and it was by postulating a fixation of the *libido* at a former stage of it that Freud explained homosexuality and also the various types of sexual neurosis.

Puberty marks the beginning of that period in life which is known as adolescence, and it is associated with very profound physiological and psychological changes. Its onset is determined by an alteration in the balance of the endocrine or ductless glands, and particularly with a marked increase in the activity of the sexual glands or gonads. The flooding of the blood stream with gonadal secretions speeds up the growth of the genitalia and accelerates also the development of the secondary sexual characteristics. These developments are associated in the girl with the beginning of the menstrual flow, and this renders the onset of puberty more abrupt for her than for her brother. But in both sexes this period is associated with the most intense bodily and psychological activity.

Puberty has sometimes been likened by psychologists to birth, and the comparison is a good one. Gerhard Adler talks of the "severing of the psychic umbilical cord connecting the growing individual with the psychic womb of the family". At puberty the young of both sexes emerge from the protecting haven of the family and are born into the bigger world of society. The awakening of sexuality, which takes place at the same time, makes this adventure of theirs still more bewildering, and it is not surprising that adolescents are often in a state of emotional instability and confusion, wanting first one thing and then another thing, pleased and upset by turns. Puberty is an exceedingly difficult time for the young of both sexes, and special allowances have to be made for those who are passing through it. They must be given plenty of time for adjusting themselves to a new and much more adult way of life, for what makes this adjustment so difficult for them is that they are themselves, continually changing owing to the greater and greater part sexuality is playing in their lives.

At adolescence the robust boy and girl friendships previously enjoyed become impossible, and a much more difficult and complicated type of relationship with the other sex begins. This change of relationship is sometimes ushered in by a period of heightened feeling for members of the same sex, by intense hero-worship on the part of the boy and by "crushes" for favourite mistresses on the part of the girl. Then this transition stage comes to an end for the great majority of girls and boys and they look with increasing favour on the opposite sex. It is all very difficult and confusing for them.

And not infrequently the emotional disturbances and irritation of this period of life are more than just difficult and confusing. Lack of control is as characteristic of adolescence as it is of infancy and in some adolescents this complete lack of inner discipline is very marked. A boy who five years previously was carrying off most of the prizes at his school may now become lazy, untidy and quarrelsome and may thereby forfeit the merit he had previously gained. His handwriting is now abominable, his attention at classes non-existent and his behaviour at home as unsatisfactory as is his behaviour at school. Or a boy who up till now has been docile and friendly with everybody may be drawn into a gang which takes delight in irritating passers-by and in damaging public property. Vague sexual upsurges from below take a hundred different forms, ranging from stealing to aggressiveness and attacks on girls.

The adolescent girl also has her troubles which often show themselves as a vague desire to stay out late at night, seeking to find something about which even she herself is far from clear. For the girl as well as for the boy adolescence is a confusing, troublesome and undisciplined time of life. One of the chief characteristics is its quick changes of moods; periods of exhilaration and sensibility alternate with dark moods of introspective doubt and severe self-criticism. Never for very long does the adolescent girl or boy remain the same, a fact which is generally as puzzling to themselves as it is to other people.

Puberty is reached by different individuals and by different races at different times. In this country it usually arrives for the girl at about the age of twelve, and her adolescence may then continue up to the age of eighteen, by which time she will have become a woman. The arrival of the first menstrual flow sometimes has a profound effect on a girl and it may change quite suddenly her whole outlook on the enigma of sex. It is essential, therefore, that she should be warned beforehand by her mother, or by some other responsible person, about what will shortly happen to her. Otherwise she may be deeply shocked and ashamed by what is an entirely natural phenomenon. The physiological meaning of the flow should also be explained to to her, as well as the hygiene to be employed at those times so that she will be completely prepared for it when it arrives.

Emphasis should always be laid on the normality of the monthly periods, and when they have begun the girl's habits of living should be altered as little as possible. It is very necessary to stress normality and naturalness in connexion with the periods, because the adjective "unwell," so often used to describe them, conjures up in the adolescent's mind ideas of illness rather than of normality.

The psychological accompaniments of puberty and adolescence are as striking as are the physical changes. Up till now the girl has taken only a theoretical interest in the relationship between the two sexes, but now she begins to wonder how all these things are going to affect her life. It is this semi-awareness of sexuality, as something which is beginning to concern her vitally as a person, which partly accounts for her shyness in the presence of her elders and of her old boy friends, a shyness which sometimes covers itself up with outbursts of gauche laughter and giggling.

But closely linked with the embarrassment and the shyness there is a steadily increasing sense of independence, together with a new capacity to criticize the adults in the home, and, more especially the chief representative of her own sex in the house, her mother. Hitherto the girl has looked up to her mother as a pattern of all that is best in womanhood and has copied her ways, but now a reaction begins to show itself. This reaction may be so strong that she becomes rebellious or even impertinent to both her parents, and by this behaviour she may cause them much concern. It is often very difficult for parents to understand the changes occurring in their daughter at such times but they should realize that she is in a troublesome transition stage and is engaged in developing qualities which in a few years will be invaluable. A great many deep-seated psychological factors are at work in the adolescent girl to account for her erratic behaviour and for her emotional outbursts, and amongst them is sometimes a feeling of envy and jealousy. In the past her mother has represented to her feminine achievement and she may now, for a period, become jealous of her. But this feeling of envy is only one of the many factors which may be at work in her subconscious mind during this period of strained relationship with her parents.

The boy's introduction to adolescence is, psychologically speaking, less abrupt than that of the girl, but there are many similarities in the adolescence of the two sexes. As the girl is upset by the start of the menstrual flow, so also is the boy liable to be disturbed by the beginning of sexual emissions whilst he is asleep. He may develop the same feeling of guilt that is felt by the boy who has been masturbating, and sometimes he actually looks upon the emissions as a subtle form of punishment for having occasionally given way to masturbation. Consequently it is much better that the boy should know beforehand that spontaneous emissions will begin in him sooner or later and that when they come they are only a sign of his changing from a boy into a man.

There exists, and has always existed, a superstition that the semen is a very vital fluid, the loss of which is enervating and even dangerous to the male. In consequence of this widespread belief, many youths are gravely disturbed by what they take to be excessive seminal losses during sleep. Now it is quite true that semen is a vital fluid, since the survival of the race is entirely dependent on it, but it is much more vital to the race than to the individual. The secretion which is essential to the health of the individual male is not the external excretion or semen, but the internal secretion of the testicles. This hormone passes back into the blood stream, and it is necessary to the maintenance of health and virility. The adolescent youth should therefore be told, just as the adolescent girl has been told, that the "losses" which he is experiencing are natural losses which will cause him no harm.

As with the girl, marked psychological changes occur in the boy with the onset of puberty. Such psychological traits as an admiration for physical courage and a love of adventure are likely to increase in him about this time, His advances into the world of the spirit may also lead to the development in him of many new ideals. Romance and altruism begin to appeal to him and he may dream of becoming of great service to humanity and of crusading for some great cause. For the first time he takes trouble with his appearance and may spend his pocket money on splendid ties and hair cream. He also begins to take notice of girls, as girls, and not as he formerly did, merely as possible companions, and with his tentative movements in that direction he becomes bashful.

A sympathetic attitude should always be maintained to a boy's first adventures in romantic love. Archness and banter are completely out of place here. So pernicious may they be that a well-known psychiatrist has reported that the final stage of the development of a youth's sexuality was indefinitely postponed by the fact that he had been teased as an adolescent about his little sweetheart.

The problem of masturbation in early childhood has already received attention, but something must be said about it in the later period of adolescence. Amongst the many things to be learnt from the Kinsey Report is the fact that late adolescence is the period of maximum sexual activity in the male. This being so, it is a mistake to belittle the difficulties of continence to the adolescent youth, for the adolescent is far more awake sexually than we have believed him to be. The Kinsey Report shows that 93·4 per cent of American boys have experienced a sexual orgasm by the age of fifteen; (60·2 per cent by means of masturbation, 26·2 per cent by heterosexual intercourse and 7 per cent by homosexual intercourse), and as one of the commentators on the Report has rightly said, this explodes the old idea "that sexual capacity develops rather slowly towards its maximum somewhere in the late twenties and then slowly begins to decline". Actually, sexual capacity and activity are at their highest very shortly after sexual activity has begun. This is a highly inconvenient fact which we adults and parents have avoided seeing by the well-known ostrich method of head-burying.

How can this problem of sexuality in youth be solved? I am of the opinion that it belongs to that not inconsiderable band of problems which have to be acknowledged as insoluble. A form of civilization has been evolved here, in the West, which makes it quite impossible for young men and women to marry when their sexual desire and sexual capacity are at their zenith, and since marriage is regarded as the only condition under which sexuality can function, the problem would seem to have no solution.

Love-making has always to conform to certain regulations, and since it is impossible to provide any socially approved outlets for the expression of youthful passion, the younger generation has to be left to find a way round the impasse. That it is a problem in which young women may also be involved is shown by the second Kinsey Report. This reveals the fact that 40 per cent. of young American women have indulged in heterosexual petting by the age of fifteen, and that this percentage rises to anything between 65 and 95 per cent. by the age of eighteen. The figures for sexual intercourse outside of the bonds of matrimony are also very high in the United States. Half of the girls who married at the age of twenty admitted to having had previous sexual experience, many of them with the men who subsequently became their husbands.

The "affair" is the solution chosen by many of the present generation and we older people are in no position to blame them for their choice. The world into which these young people have been born is a world of our own devising and it is a world which is controlled by material rather than by spiritual values. Religion is at such a low ebb in the West that it is almost non-existent and sexuality is deliberately used for the purpose of selling our newspapers and our goods. We must reap what we have helped to sow, a civilization almost entirely controlled by economic values, a civilization in which the old and impossible ideal of pre-marital chastity will have to be abandoned.

We older people have made much of the process known as sublimation. By this word we mean the diversion of attention and sexual energy into another and more convenient field of activity such as games, sport, outdoor exercise, or into the emotional outlets provided by art and social welfare work. But we have expected far too much of sublimation and it is unable to do all that we had hoped. Kinsey, whose conclusions on the subject of sublimation have the merit of being based on statistics rather than on personal opinion, summarizes his views on sublimation as follows:

"A great many persons have tried to establish their sexual lives on the assumption that sublimation is possible and the outcome desirable. . . . Fundamentally apathetic persons are the ones who are most often moral, (confirming to the *mores*), most insistent that it is a simple matter to control sexual response, and most likely to offer themselves as examples of the possibility of the diversion of probably non-existent sexual energies. But such inactivity is no more sublimation . . . than blindness, deafness or other perceptive defects. If . . . one removes those who are physically incapacitated, natively low in sexual drive, sexually unawakened in their younger years, separated from their usual sources of stimulation, or timid and upset by their repressions, there are simply no cases which remain as clear-cut examples of sublimation." (*Sexual Behaviour in the Human Male*, A. C. Kinsey, W. P. Pomeroy, C. E. Martin. Saunders.)

According to Kinsey therefore all that can be expected of sublimation is that it will result in the transference of a small amount of sexual energy into other fields of activity, but that it can bring about the disappearance of all sexual desire is as little to be expected of it as that any form of treatment could lead to a complete disappearance of a natural desire for food. Too much has been promised of it by our sexual reformers and according to Ouspensky the explanation of their lack of understanding is that codes of sexual behaviour are laid down not by the ruling classes of a nation acting as a whole but by a certain limited section of this class which itself suffers from the condition which Ouspensky called "infra-sex". He writes of this sexually weak and essentially abstemious section of society as follows:

"Among other people, the people of infra-sex appear the

most moral, in religion the most saintly. It is easy for them to be "moral" and it is easy for them to be saintly. Of course it is pseudo-morality and pseudo-saintliness, but people generally live with pseudo-values and only extremely few wish to find real values. It is necessary to understand that almost all the morality which has been imposed upon the human race, almost all the laws controlling sex life, almost all the restrictions guiding people's choice and decision in these cases, all taboos, all fears, all these have come from infra-sex. Infra-sex, precisely in virtue of its difference from normal sex, began to regard itself as superior, began to dictate laws to normal sex. This does not mean that all morals, all laws and restrictions relating to sex were wrong. But as always occurs in life when right ideas come from the wrong source, together with what is right they bear within them a great deal that is wrong, that contradicts their essence, that brings about new confusions and new complications". (P. D. Ouspensky, *A New Model of the Universe*. London, 1938, Kegan Paul.)

My own observations, so far as they go, would seem to support Ouspensky's views that many of the members of watch committees and vigilance societies, which have been established in order to keep an eye on the sexual behaviour of other people are representative of what Ouspensky calls infra-sex. I am of the opinion that many of the bitterest opponents of those unfortunate people, the homosexuals, have homosexual leanings themselves. They vindicate their own homosexuality by the fierceness with which they denounce homosexuality in other people. A good example of the tendency of people of infra-sex to concern themselves with the sexual behaviour of others is provided by the celebrated American Purity Campaigner, Comstock, who devoted his life to the detection of supposedly obscene literature, an occupation which gave him an outlet for his own thwarted sexuality. As Dr. Alex Comfort has pointed out: "In the wider sense it is generally admitted frustration of extreme feelings of guilt to sexual matters may lead to the development of a particular form of aggressive conduct which manifests itself in the desire for unlimited authority. There is a growing suggestion in the available evidence that while membership of a ruling class depends upon economic circumstance, the desire to govern, especially in highly centralized communities, is a manifestation of this type of aggression. Kinsey compared the moral attitude of a known group of individuals with their mean frequencies of sexual outlet, and noted that the demands made by each for the exercise of restriction and of abstinence by others, and by society, were almost exactly in inverse proportion to their own sexual requirements". (Alex Comfort, *Sexual Behaviour in Society*. Gerald Duckworth, London.)

Primitive people handle the problem of the sexual needs of their adolescents in ways not dissimilar to those which the younger members of western society are now finding out for themselves. Emotional and sexual maturity are reached earlier in tropical countries but as in these lands marriage can also take place at an earlier age the problem remains the same. In a few of these more backward countries full intercourse is permitted and we have some evidence that during this period of adolescent mate-selection a low degree of fertility exists so that conception occurs only rarely. Other countries tolerate a number of sexual practices which stop short of full intercourse, and which resemble very closely the practices now being adopted by the younger generation in America. Similar practices have, of course, long been tolerated in certain sections of our own society, one example of them being the Welsh custom known as "Courting on the bed".

Two types of argument have been brought against such behaviour on the part of adolescents, the one moral and the other physiological. I have myself raised a physiological objection against "petting" since it may interfere with the attainment of satisfactory and maturer forms of sexual response at a later date. But it is only fair to say that statistics obtained from the Kinsey Report do not support this view. Kinsey even goes so far as to say that there is evidence that "petting may improve the effectiveness of sexual relationships after marriage". Terman, on the other hand, disagrees with this view of Kinsey's and produces certain evidence to the effect that petting is more likely to do harm than good. The most probable explanation of this disagreement between experts is that much will depend on the attitude of the experimenters to petting. Fear, a feeling of guilt and a failure to obtain sexual satisfaction in this way are likely to give rise to anxiety and to an increase rather than a release of emotional tension. In such circumstances petting is likely to be followed by bad results but in their absence it may well prove harmless.

The moral argument lodged against these sexual practices is that they are incitements to complete intercourse and consequently "playing with fire". But the Kinsey Report does not bear out this statement that petting acts as an incitement to coitus, for amongst the more highly educated adolescents, where petting was a common practice, the incidence of pre-marital coitus was low, whereas amongst the less well-educated adolescents, where petting was comparatively rare, pre-marital coitus was much commoner.

19

SEX EDUCATION

IF what was stated in the earlier chapters of this book be true, ~~that ninety per cent of the sexual difficulties in marriage are~~ psychological in origin and are the results of faulty attitudes to sexuality acquired in childhood, then the sex education of children is a subject of immense importance. Fortunately, this is now widely realized and during the last fifty years efforts have been made to avoid the terrible errors committed in the past. The Victorian nursery was a veritable seed bed for sexual neuroses which came to maturity in later years. Victorian parents and nurses felt that it was impossible to be too drastic in inculcating sound moral principles into the young, and the word "moral" was being used by them as synonymous with sexual morality. Adolescents were told therefore that masturbation was a sin which might lead to madness or blindness. It was never left unpunished so that if madness or blindness did not follow, then an All-loving Deity had in store for the sinner a still more appropriate punishment in the form of impotence for the male and damaged children for the female. Gynaecologists of today tell us that the fear that the punishment for self-abuse will be inflicted on the sinner's children still survives, and is the reason why some women are frightened of becoming pregnant. Dr. Joan Malleson also describes a case in which an elderly patient refused to use the vaginal ring she had been ordered as a remedy for a prolapsed uterus because she had been warned as a child never to touch those parts of herself.

Even if the parents realize how very important instruction on the subject of sex is to their children, it is impossible for them to be sure that fear and guilt will not be instilled into them by some other adult or even by a child, for children often discuss their dreads and their nightmares with their friends. And, as we have seen, these early childish fears may be responsible, later in life, for a wife's failure to obtain an orgasm, and for such difficulties as premature ejaculation in her husband. Fortunately, much is now being done to reduce the incidence of these psychogenic troubles by enlightening the public on the subject of sexuality, and by giving a better education to the child, and it is with the latter that we now have to deal.

The education of the child in sexual matters should not be withheld until the right moment for enlightenment is supposed to have arrived for it, but should start with the first question asked on this subject. The last thing desirable is that the child should be led to believe that sexuality is something standing aloof from ordinary life, a queer thing which requires very special handling, and this is precisely what is implied when a special moment is selected for a talk on "the facts of life". Fortunately, those old-fashioned, sex-stained interviews between a frightened father and a slightly less frightened son, or between an equally scared mother and her daughter are becoming rarer and rarer. More often than not the children subjected to those painful interviews had already heard all about the facts of life from their friends, and were perplexed only because their parents were making such a song and dance about them. No, it is not the parents who decide when sexual instruction has to begin but the child—and this is just as it should be.

The first question likely to be put to the mother is when the child is at a very tender age and this is the signal for the start of his sex education. To the child of four, five or six the world is a vast collection of puzzles to be looked at and solved, and amongst the many things to be found out is how things begin. It is a great mistake therefore to avoid answering some of the more awkward questions put to a parent, either by trailing a red herring across the track or else by promising to answer a little later when he or she will be able to understand things better. It is a mistake because this will arouse suspicions in the child that there is some mystery behind all this hedging. He will acquire a feeling that whilst it is quite right and proper to talk about most things, there are certain subjects which must on no account be mentioned, and if anything is calculated to give a fillip to his curiosity it is this. Even a change in his mother's voice or a startled expression whilst parrying what she regards as being an undesirable question, is quite enough to stimulate his curiosity on that subject and to make him ask for more.

No, the teaching of the young child should consist of an honest discussion of facts and should be devoid of all feeling of awkwardness on the parent's part. There is no awkwardness in the question for the child and all that he has asked for is to have his curiosity satisfied. If this is done quite naturally he will in all probability pass quickly on to another subject. The main requirement is that the answer should be true so that nothing he has learnt will have to be unlearnt at a later date. It never pays to deceive a child. He is bound sooner or later to discover the falsity of his mother's information and will quite rightly lose confidence in her.

The answer must, of course, be as simple a one as possible, an answer which is necessarily incomplete but is sufficient for the purposes of the moment. Children accept a simple statement of fact quite naturally and having attached no particular importance to their question, they attribute no special significance to the answer. A child has an unsullied mind on everything connected with sexuality, an attitude he will maintain until embarrassment and shame have been implanted into his mind by someone else. This delightfully simple and straight-forward attitude of the child to sex sometimes comes as a great relief to the mother who has braced herself to answer as truth-fully as possible what she had previously thought to be an extremely awkward question.

The first enquiries are likely to be evoked by some special event in the home, such as the arrival of a new baby or the sudden appearance of kittens, and in all probability they will be concerned with birth and motherhood. All that need be said on this subject is that up till then the baby or kitten in question has been nurtured within the body of its mother, but that now it is big enough to live in the outside world like everybody else. The child will not be surprised at this news for he will have seen mothers looking after their children. So if mothers do this after their babies have been born, why should they not do the same thing before they were born? It is all quite natural and as it should be to the child.

The problem of fatherhood is likely to come later, and ques-tions about it are a little more difficult to answer. A lecture on fertilization in terms of flowers and bees is quite useless and is more likely to puzzle than to enlighten the child. Some parents venture a little further into the realm of biology, and introduce the idea of fatherhood by talking about fertilized and unferti-lized eggs in the hope that the child will carry on this line of thought himself. But the child is too literal to be able to do this. For him flowers are flowers and eggs are eggs and there is no connexion at all between flowers and eggs and the fathers of kittens and babies. But he has realized by now that all children have fathers as well as mothers, and that children can take after their fathers in the same way that they can take after their mothers. In order to account for this the question of mating has to be brought in sooner or later. This will be made much easier for the parent if the child has visited a farmyard, at some time or another, and still easier if he is having elementary biology lessons at school. By satisfying the child's curiosity concerning the rôle of the father, and explaining that it is through the action of the father that everything begins, the subject of the reproduction of animals will have been rounded off. The child will then have learnt that the kitten or the baby grew inside the body of its mother, and he will know also something about why it began to grow there. In all probability he will now lose interest in a subject which is not very thrilling and rather complicated.

Marjorie Hume, formerly secretary of the Marriage Guidance Council, points out that by keeping the explanation of conception and birth entirely on the animal plane, as we have so far been doing in this description, there is a danger that the child will be left with the notion that human love is a purely animal process, and that this will be an obstacle to his attaining a right attitude to sexuality and marriage later on in life. In my opinion this danger is not a very serious one and can easily be averted. The original answers can always be supplemented afterwards by statements on the subject of human love and of spiritual values if this is felt to be necessary. It would have been a mistake to have made the first answers too complicated for the child's understanding and it is much better to correct wrong impressions at a later date after the child has made a better acquaintance with the world of the spirit.

Home instruction in sex is greatly helped if the child is having what are known as "nature studies" at school. The importance of biology in the education of the child is now much more generally recognized than it formerly was. Not only is more time allotted in the school curriculum to lessons on this subject, but teachers are better equipped for giving them. At present there is some difference of opinion amongst educational authorities as to the advisability or not of adding to the course of general biology special talks on the subject of human reproduction, and experiments are being made in the hope of determining which is the better plan. In any case parents would be wise to find out from the school authorities precisely what instruction is being given to their children at school, and if they are in doubt and this be possible, they should discuss with the biology teacher how home instruction can best be linked up with what is being learnt in school. Whatever the arrangements finally made, it should be born in mind that however good school biology classes may be, they cannot compete in importance with the attitude to sexuality of those living in the child's home. A child is far more sensitive to the home atmosphere than most people realize, and whatever parents may say, it is what they *are* which counts with him. Children cannot analyse and formulate their feelings but emotionally they are usually very discerning.

Parents should be specially on the watch for the signs of puberty in their older children and should be ready to supplement the general sexual instruction already given, with special advice about the changes occurring at that time. It is better that the father should talk to the adolescent son and not the mother, for the awakening in him of sexual feeling and the onset of such phenomena as nocturnal emissions in him makes the boy shy of talking about such matters to a woman, even though the woman be his mother. Moreover the boy knows that the father was once in the same position as himself and that he will, therefore, be able to understand him better. In short, this is a subject to be discussed between one man and another in a matter of fact way and the wider the range of this conversation between the two males the better. It may also be an appropriate occasion for speaking to the boy about the opposite sex and particularly about the occurrence of menstruation in girls. He will thereby be saved from asking awkward questions in public about a sister or a friend who is unable every now and then to go for a swim or to take active exercise with him. Moreover it is just as well that he should know that women have certain physical burdens to bear from which men are exempt, and that it is only fair that men should show them special consideration at such times. The fact that women have gained political equality with men does not necessarily mean that chivalry is now an anachronism.

Although the sex education of the child has started with the infant's first question, and has continued without interruption ever since, there commonly arises a time in a boy's career when a special talk on sexual problems is called for. The moment when this seems to be appropriate will vary in different cases but perhaps the most useful time will be when the boy is well advanced in adolescence and on the point of entering some career. It is at such a time that sexuality is likely to be forcing itself on his attention and to be making life difficult for him. But what form should such a conversation between father and son take?

It is no easy matter this talk about the management of sexuality and about the ins and outs of sexual ethics. We are all familiar with the form these talks took in the past with both parties feeling a little uncomfortable and with the father struggling hard to drop the heavy rôle of the parent and to appear at his ease and not too pious. "Of course, I quite understand how you feel, my boy, for I can well remember how things were with me when I was your age. I know how strong the sex urge can be in a boy and how easily he may be led to do things he will afterwards regret. These sexual feelings are of course entirely natural and there is nothing reprehensible in them at all. They are the earliest stirrings of an impulse which will not reach its full flowering in you for years to come and in the meantime you can look upon them as a valuable means of learning self-discipline. Some day you will marry and have children of your own, but now all your thoughts and your efforts must be directed to the task of equipping yourself for your career. When you are in a position to support a wife and a family the right girl will come along and, having kept yourself from temptation and led a clean life, you will be worthy of her love."

This sort of speech was perhaps a little stilted but it avoided such ridiculous expressions as "treating every girl as you would treat your sister", and it was satisfactory so far as it went, provided that the premises on which it was based were sound. But was that bit about the youth's experiencing the first stirrings of a function which would not reach maturity for many years to come really true? No, it was based on an entirely fictitious biology, which happened to come in handy at that moment. Actually the boy being admonished was nearing the zenith of his sexual capacity and at an earlier epoch in history he would have already been married to a girl of fourteen about to produce her first child. The great lovers of history, the Romeos and Juliets, and the Aucassions and Nicolettes were still in their teens and as Peter Fletcher has put it, what we are now requiring of our young people "is not that they should refrain from eating unripe fruit, but that they should leave the ripe fruit on the tree untouched till after it has passed its prime". (*Sex and Society*. Kenneth Walker and Peter Fletcher. Pelican.)

What makes the situation still more difficult for us parents of today is that we are forced to continue giving this kind of advice even after we have discovered the falseness of its biological premises. Because modern conditions make it difficult or impossible for young men to support a family until they are in the neighbourhood of thirty, and because most of us subscribe to the idea that love-making outside the bonds of matrimony is wrong, anti-social, unethical or whatever we prefer to term it, we have no alternative to that of continuing the fiction that our sons will not attain full sexual maturity until they are economically in a position to maintain a wife and a family. Yet the truth of the matter is that by the time the young man is economically in a position to maintain a wife his sexual capacity will have begun to decline.

For the moralist sublimation is the only right and proper solution to the problem of youthful sexuality. Sublimation is a blessed word in time of trouble, but does sublimation actually possess the magic with which it is credited? To some youths it may afford a little help but the strains and stresses of the highly sexed young man will never be entirely resolved by it. Sublimation means the transformation of the sexual impulses or *libido*, in its narrower sense, into some higher psychic activity with the result that the lower activity ceases for the moment to be all compelling. So the schoolmaster encourages his older pupils to devote themselves wholeheartedly to their games and to think of nothing else but games, sportsmanship and the team spirit; whilst the clergyman lays before his young parishioners the over-riding claims of religion. And as has already been said both of these remedies may prove helpful up to a point but to claim that they will ever afford complete relief from the nagging hunger of sex is absurd.

Havelock Ellis suggests that the word chastity has been far too narrowly interpreted. It is generally used to denote complete sexual abstinence and it is also tacitly assumed that complete abstinence is always a virtue whatever the motives for it may happen to be. But as Flaubert once remarked in a letter to George Sand it is only the effort to remain chaste which is likely to do good and not the result of the effort. There is no virtue in refraining entirely from food although a short bout of starvation may sometimes be beneficial to an individual and for this reason Havelock Ellis prefers to define chastity not as sexual abstinence but as "self-control within the sexual field". Chastity, in this sense of the word, can be accepted by all of us as a positive virtue. It is an ideal which would also be acceptable to all cultures from the most primitive to the most complex.

Another point which requires stressing here is that abstinence from sexual intercourse does not necessarily mean chastity, even in the restricted sense in which Havelock Ellis uses that word. A youth may be wallowing in a state of voluptuous imagination, mentally undressing every girl he meets and masturbating daily or even twice daily, even although he is avoiding all sexual intercourse. Yet such a youth as this can scarcely be said to be "controlling himself within the sexual field". Indeed a youth of this kind can make no claim to virtue of any kind at all, for if the motive behind his refraining from sexual intercourse be looked into more carefully it will usually be found to be a fear motive of one kind or another. He is not refraining from sexual intercourse for the sake of some lofty ideal but because he is frightened of being found out by his parents, or is frightened of scandal, or of proving inadequate as a man. Now hard as the lot of a highly sexed youth may be who sacrifices his sexuality for the sake of some religious ideal it is incomparably easier than the lot of a youth who has sacrificed sexuality for no real reason of his own at all. Tossed between the desire for sexual satisfaction and fear of the consequences of finding an outlet for it he is subjected to unceasing strain, from which he may break down.

All youths do not suffer to this extent from the forcible suppression of their sexual function, for the strength of sexuality varies widely in different individuals. The payment therefore that the individual has to make for remaining continent may be anything from zero to a hundred and this fact will have to be borne in mind by a father discussing the subject of sexual control with his son.

What advice should such a father give his boy when the latter has reached say the age of twenty, and is leaving home to fend for himself? Few generalizations can be made on this subject of paternal advice, for what the father says will depend entirely on his own experience and on his own sexual ethics. The writer of this book can only describe the lines along which he personally would talk if confronted with this problem. His first endeavour would be to help his son to review the situation as a whole for himself in order that he might be able to reach *his own* conclusions and not necessarily those of his parents. He would caution him against adopting any programme blindly, whether it were the Church's rules for sexual behaviour or the code of behaviour adopted by his companions in their reaction against conventional codes of morality. If it were his intention to remain chaste then it must be for the sake of a *positive* ideal and not because of some fear lurking in the background and pretending to be a virtue. He would also impress upon his son the fact that a man who puts aside sex for the sake of some ideal always has to make certain payments, for ideals can never be served without some form of sacrifice. If on the other hand he did not intend to make sacrifices he would have to realize the fact that sexuality can never be allowed complete freedom to express itself as it likes but must always be subjected to certain rules. He would suggest to the boy that the first of these rules was that he must never take his own pleasure at the expense of someone else, for sexual intercourse should be a communion between two people who were endeavouring to satisfy each other's sexual needs. What a man obtained from his sexuality would depend entirely on his attitude to it. If for him it were only a bodily function, like eating and drinking, then sexuality for that man would never be more than this. If for another man it was merely a ribald joke then a ribald joke it would remain for him to the end of his days.

Only if a man used this mysterious gift of sexuality carefully and reverently would he be able to obtain from it some of the richest experiences in life. It is along such lines as these that the author of this book would talk to a grown up son about to set foot on the highway of adult life.

And what of a daughter? Since equality has been accorded to women in all spheres of activity it must be also accorded to them in the realm of sex. If freedom is to be given to a son to find his own way through the problems of sex a similar freedom must be accorded to the daughter. In sex, as in other things, daughters and sons must enjoy equality but it must always be remembered that it is man and not Providence that has arrived at this doctrine of the *equality* of men and women in the sphere of sexuality. Nature is of a contrary power and Nature has penalized women from the very start. For a woman sexual intercourse entails far greater commitments than it does for a man and in embarking on it she is taking far higher risks. She must ponder over the matter therefore much more carefully than does the man. So also must she take into consideration the fact that the urge in her to defy the laws of propriety is likely to be much less insistent than is the same urge in her brother. Being less blindly driven than he is she has been accorded a greater measure of choice. All this must she take into consideration before committing herself to an action she may later regret.

The Western ban on sexual intercourse outside the sphere of marriage applies much more strongly to women than to men, but in spite of the greater equality exacted of them the women of today are frequently defying it. Terman's researches show a very marked difference between the pre-marital histories of middle-aged and of young wives. On questioning a number of wives of different ages, he found that the percentage of them who came to their marriages as virgins fell steeply between the years 1910 and 1930. As the outcome of this research on the pre-marital chastity of American wives he came to the following conclusion: "If the drop should continue at the average rate shown for those born since 1890, virginity at marriage will be close to vanishing point for males born after 1930 and for females born after 1940. It is more likely that the rate of change will become somewhat retarded as the zero point is approached and that an occasional virgin will come to the marriage bed for a few decades beyond the date indicated by the curve. It will be of no small interest to see how long the cultural ideal of the virgin marriage will survive as a moral code after its observance has passed into history." (L. M. Terman, *Psychological Factors in Marital Behaviour*, 1938.)

So whatever the nature of the speech given by the father to his son or his daughter on reaching adult life, the younger generation are finding their own answers to this problem and this is as it should be. It is in their hands that the future lies.

20

BREAKING AND BROKEN MARRIAGES

DR. EUSTACE CHESSER has just completed a statistical survey of marriage and his report shows that the success or failure of the marriage would seem to depend, to a great extent, on the closeness of the relationship the wife has established with her husband. The happily married woman almost invariably volunteered the statement that she was as much in love with her husband now as she had been when she first married him and that she would marry him again if she were to meet him as an unmarried girl. The reverse was true of the unhappily married woman who was also a disillusioned woman, bitterly disappointed with her husband. Three-quarters of the unhappily married women said that if given another chance they would marry an entirely different kind of man, whilst the remaining quarter said that if they were free they would never marry again.

There was a substantial difference between the happily and the unhappily married groups of women with regard to their opinions as to their similarities and dissimilarities with their husbands. "The majority (over two-thirds) of those with exceptionally or very happy marriages felt that they were very like their husbands in mutual affection, sense of humour and ambitions, whereas only a small minority (one-eighth or less) of those having unhappy marriages felt this. Another characteristic of most (three-fifths or more) of the exceptionally or very happy marriages was that they usually or invariably agreed with their husbands on the subject of holidays, how to run the house and how to look after the children. Only one-seventh of the unhappily married women were in harmony with their husbands on these subjects."

The survey included also an enquiry as to the part played by sexual satisfaction in rendering a marriage happy or unhappy. But in an investigation of this kind there is always the difficulty of deciding which is cause and which is effect, in other words whether a satisfactory sexual relationship between a man and his wife is the *result* of their happiness in marriage or its cause. All that Dr. Eustace Chesser can tell us on this important subject is that the two extreme groups (of happiness and unhappiness in marriage) "differed as regards the amount of sexual satisfaction that they had obtained. One-half of the exceptionally, or very happily married couples had achieved a great deal of satisfaction in sexual intercourse with their husbands whilst only one-tenth of the wives in the unhappily married group were sexually satisfied. The general attitude to sexual intercourse in the two groups was also different. Few, if any, of the happily married women ever refused their husbands sexual intercourse, whereas one-quarter of the unhappily married women frequently declined intercourse."

This is as we should expect it to be, that wives in successful marriages have a much greater measure of agreement with their husbands than have wives in unsuccessful marriages; but although to us this may be an obvious truism it is not always apparent to the married couples themselves. As a medical man I am continually being consulted by husbands about their sexual difficulties with their wives, when all that is really wrong with them is that *they are no longer in love with their wives*. And what is of great interest is that their bodies are always much quicker in discovering this fact than they are themselves. "I am devoted to my wife", a patient will protest a little too earnestly perhaps, but he is entirely mistaken in this. His mind has mistaken loyalty and a sense of duty for love but his body realizes that he has lost his heart to someone else, to his secretary perhaps or to his friend's wife. And knowing the truth his body refuses to obey his mind's orders, to the effect that for reasons of domestic policy it is desirable to continue making nominal love to his wife. The patient may either still be in the dark about the true state of affairs or else he may be deliberately avoiding seeing the truth. The truth is by no means always welcome to us when we are trying to maintain the fiction that all is well with our world.

Although man has attained control over many things which lie outside him, he has very little control over himself and none at all over those erratic things his emotions. But he is usually quite unaware of his inner state and fondly imagines that he is master of his various emotions and functions, including that most insubordinate of activities, his sexual function. For some reason, other than love, it is advisable that he should meet the sexual needs of his wife and maintain the integrity of the home but to his consternation he finds that he is no longer able to do this. So he hurries off to consult an expert about his impotence. The following report from my files shows how blind men may be about the true state of their feelings and how easily they may be bamboozled by their heads.

Mr. X is a corn merchant of forty-nine years of age who is now suffering from partial impotence. He has three children, has been married twenty years and has noted a gradual weakening of his potency during the last five years. On being asked about his relationship with his wife, he admits that there have been frequent rows between them and also rows between himself and his wife's people. Periodically she makes a gesture of leaving him and in case he should try to detain her by force she takes the precaution of telephoning for the village policeman. At this point I interrupted his story and enquired bluntly whether he was any longer in love with his wife and he replied without hesitation "No". I then asked him if his wife were any longer in love with him, to which he returned an equally emphatic negative. But because this otherwise intelligent man had thought it right and proper to carry on the fiction of "making love" to his wife and because his body would play no part in the mockery he had found it necessary to come to London for treatment of his impotence. "Lord, what fools these mortals be".

I cannot believe that a woman is ever so blind to the real state of her feelings as a man can be and often is. Many wives know in their hearts that they are no longer in love with their husbands, in the sense in which they formerly were in love with them, but because there is much of great value in their marriage they submit to their husband's embraces whether they enjoy them or not, keeping their secret to themselves. And it is right that they should do this for there may be many things of the greatest value left in a marriage after all sexual attraction has departed from it. One of the lessons to be derived from a study of Dr. Chesser's painstaking survey of marriage is that the success and happiness of a marriage is made up, not of one or two, but of a great many different varieties of ingredients. It is the whole pattern of a couple's relationship with each other which counts, and the importance of each of the many ingredients in this relationship can only be assessed by relating it to this whole pattern. When therefore we are investigating such a subject as happiness in marriage we have to include in our survey not only the success of the couple in adjusting themselves to each other but their success in adjusting themselves to life.

Some of the difficulties and errors which cause unhappiness in marriage have already been mentioned and suggestions have been given as to how best they can be dealt with. The following causes of unhappiness in marriage were derived from a Gallup Poll taken a few years ago and quoted in Sir Adolphe Abraham's book. The complaints voiced by unhappily married women were as follows:

Complaints that there was insufficient scope for romance whilst they were running a home and a family.

Lack of interests in common with their husbands.

Religious differences between them and their husbands.

Insufficient in common to keep the marriage going after it had been found that they would never be able to have children.

Disapproval of the husband or of the wife by the parents-in-law.

Clashes on the subject of money.

Irritation with the husband's or the wife's personal habits and peculiarities.

Differences in the social backgrounds of the two marriage partners.

Difficulties in connexion with birth control methods.

Complaints that the temperament of the partner was such that it was impossible to continue to live with him or her.

Drunkenness.

(N.B. It was generally agreed by the wives that the infidelity of their husbands was only the outward sign that the marriage had gone wrong and not the actual cause of its going wrong.)

America does everything on a big scale and an investigation of 1,500 marriages produced 500 pages of facts concerning the more important disruptive forces in marriage. Sexual difficulties are not included in the following lists as they have been dealt with in other chapters and it should be noted that the objections lodged by dissatisfied husbands against their wives and of dissatisfied wives against their husbands are given in the order of their frequency.

Complaints made by husbands against their wives: That they were continually nagging; That they showed no affection; That they were selfish; That they interfered with their husband's hobbies; That they had become slovenly in their appearance;

That they interfered with the disciplining of the family; That they were unduly critical of their husbands; That they neglected the children; That they were poor housekeepers.

Complaints made by wives against their husbands: That they were extremely inconsiderate; That they mismanaged financial matters; That they were untruthful; That they showed no affection; That they would never "talk things over"; That they were too hard on the children; That they were very "touchy"; That they showed no interest in the home; That they lacked all ambition; That they were rude.

When we study these lists of complaints we see how trivial most of them are, trivial at any rate at the start, although they may afterwards have grown formidable. One has the feeling that if only the difficulties between the couples had been taken early and an attempt had been made to remedy them, the marriage might have been saved. But unfortunately our habits grow as quickly as do weeds and although, at the start, our partners are able to put up with them, in the course of time they become quite unbearable. "I shall scream if you do that again", shouts the exasperated wife, and the husband, unable to stand any more of her screaming and nagging, slams the door and goes out for the rest of that evening. Each of the complaints conjures up before our eyes a domestic tragi-comedy on which the curtain might have been rung down at the end of the first act if only some wise person had acted as impartial referee, or if the leading actors had sat down and talked things over together and come to some amicable conclusion on the subject. But alas by the time that the third act had been reached there was nothing for the two chief actors to do except to part!

Something must be said on the subject of infidelity as a cause of divorce. It is obvious that adultery on the part either of the husband or wife throws a great strain on a marriage but too much emphasis has been placed on it by the Church and by the

Law as grounds for divorce. Both of these institutions have taken an unduly serious view of adultery and in the eyes of the Law it constitutes the main reason for terminating a marriage. Yet, as we have seen, infidelity usually represents the final collapse of a marriage which was in any case nearing the point of breaking, and is rarely the primary cause of its breaking. But because society has been taught both by the Church and the Law to look with such intense horror on adultery, there is little or no hope of saving a marriage in which adultery has occurred. Even if the two persons concerned do not consult their solicitors immediately the scandalized relatives are likely to insist that this should be done and that the conduct of the guilty party should on no account be condoned. Now it is quite true that a wife or husband cannot be otherwise than hurt by the news that her or his partner is having an affair, but intense resentment and immediate resort to the divorce courts can scarcely be regarded as ideal responses to such news. As Alex Comfort has remarked, one of the chief tasks of marriage guidance councils is to prevent belligerent relatives from intruding in this way and wrecking all attempts to bring about a reconciliation. Such marriages can only be saved by trying to dissipate the idea that immediate divorce is obligatory, by increasing respect for the personal freedom of both parties, by emphasizing the importance of understanding a partner rather than of insisting on personal rights, and above all by trying to ensure that specific situations of this kind are considered on the same level as that at which other personal problems are considered, and not on a higher emotional level. "If we can induce husbands and wives to regard one another as human beings whose conduct is comprehensible and remove what may be called the operatic aspect of marriage, we can do a great deal to reduce emotional difficulties of this kind to the level of other personal problems. Jealousy is compatible up to a point, with mutual respect, and no amount of psychology will draw the teeth of the emotional problems . . . of two people over a long period; but there are signs that, left alone by society, the partners will settle their difficulties more easily than when they are subject to social and moral pressure." (Alex Comfort, *Sexual Behaviour in Society*. Gerald Duckworth.)

No two people can live together without misunderstandings occasionally arising and too much importance should not be attributed to the usual distempers of married life. But as illnesses do not always yield to medical remedies so also does it sometimes happen that marriage difficulties do not yield to ordinary forms of treatment. Because of their intractability an operation may have to be carried out and the operation required for a desperately sick marriage is the radical one of divorce. This is a book on love, marriage and the family, but as marriages sometimes end in failure the subject of divorce must also be included in our survey.

Marriage was originally instituted for the sake of the children resulting from it and if the contract between the two parents has to be terminated the interests of the children must still remain their first consideration. "How will it affect them and if a divorce has to be gone through when would it be best to arrange it? Would it be better to postpone this final step until they have reached an age when they will be able to understand better what has happened or should it be taken now?" These are the kind of questions which the husband and wife will have to put to each other and answer.

Many things will have to be taken into consideration in arriving at a decision and amongst them the fact that children are far more vitally affected by what their parents actually are, and by how they behave, than by what they say. Children are sensitive to a tense atmosphere in the home and their powers of observation are far keener than is generally supposed.

This being so they feel and suffer from the lack of harmony in their parents even though no words have passed between them. Jung has laid great emphasis on the way in which the tensions in the unconscious parts of the parent's minds act upon the unconscious parts of the child's mind. "The child", he writes "is so much a part of the psychic atmosphere of his parents that secret and unsolved trouble between them can influence a child's health profoundly. The *participation mystique* which is the primitive unconscious identity of the child with its parents, causes the child to feel the conflcts of its parents and to suffer for them, as if they were its own troubles. It is hardly ever the open conflicts or the manifest difficulties that have the poisonous effect; it is almost always a disharmony repressed and neglected of the parents. The real cause of such a disturbance is, without exception, the unconscious. It is a thing vaguely felt by the child, the oppressive atmosphere of apprehension and self-consciousness that slowly pervades the child's mind like a poisonous vapour and destroys the security of the conscious adaptation."

A practical demonstration of the effect of maladjustment of the parents on the child is only too commonly provided us by an examination of neurotic and delinquent children; and even when the tension in the home has not been sufficient to produce such serious results as these, in the children it may account for a great deal of moodiness and fearfulness in the child—a fearfulness which rapidly disappears when he is removed from the unfavourable environment and placed in tranquil and secure surroundings. This being so, the health and happiness of the child must be given first prime consideration when the question of divorce or separation is being discussed by the parents.

That divorce is a remedy which is being more and more frequently adopted for unhappy marriages is obvious from the Registrar General's returns for England and Wales. In 1930 there were 315,109 marriages and 3,482 divorces, that is to say a ratio of one divorce to every 100 marriages. In 1949 there were 375,041 marriages and 34,217 divorces, or one divorce to every 10 marriages. Another marked change is also apparent in these 1949 figures, namely that many more wives are providing their husbands with the grounds for divorce. Fifty years ago the husband almost always played the part of the guilty party, whether he were actually guilty or not, but now women appear in this rôle more frequently than men do. In 1938, 4,649 petitions were filed by husbands and 5,321 by wives, but in 1947, 28,749 petitions were filled by husbands and only 18,292 by wives.

Many factors other than unhappiness in marriage are probably responsible for the steep rise in the incidence of divorce during the last thirty years and an important one is a change in our attitude to divorce. When the author of this book was a boy divorce was looked upon as being almost as disgraceful as theft and few respectable people would care to be seen speaking to a divorced woman. This ultra-respectability has gone and Ministers of State and men and women of the highest standing and integrity can pass through the divorce court without anything being said against them. The stigma has been almost entirely removed from divorce so that men and women have recourse to it without hesitation when their marriages have reached the stage of being no longer workable.

Another reason for this increase of divorce has already been given, namely that modern women demand far more of marriage than their grandmothers did. A hundred years ago marriage was the only career open to a girl and she embarked on it prepared to take all the risks that it entailed for her. Even if she were unlucky in her husband she would have a home and a family of her own and for the sake of these she would put up with his shortcomings. But the women of today have other views of marriage. Many alternative careers are open to them so that they are not nearly so dependent on marriage as their grandmothers were. If the women of today marry and the marriage is not a success they can get a divorce and either marry somebody else, or else can make their own living. Yet another factor in the rise of divorce is that the grounds for it have been extended and this, together with the provision of free legal aid has brought divorce within the reach of almost everybody.

Divorce laws vary very widely in different countries but they usually have this in common, that they are both archaic and chaotic. This is particularly true of the Divorce Laws of the United States of America, where a man can get a divorce and remarry in one State, only to find that his divorce is not recognized in another State, and that if he elects to live there he will be in the position of a man who has contracted a bigamous marriage. Yet, in spite of the fact that this confusion in the divorce laws is widely recognized by the legal authorities, any attempt to bring about a reform in them is immediately met with the fiercest opposition.

The reason for this becomes apparent when we examine the history of our own divorce laws. They were framed originally for the purpose of settling the disposition of the property of the contracting parties and also for defining the position of the guilty party as regards inheritance. They also settled the respective rights of the father and mother to possess or to have access, in the case of a divorce, to the children. When, therefore, a man and woman married they entered into a legal contract with each other and if, at a later date, they broke this contract some sort of provision had to be made for their breach of faith. Consequently the divorce laws are chiefly concerned with the disposal of property after the divorce. But during the Middle Ages the Church acquired control over the institution of marriage and converted what had previously been only a legal con-

tract into a sacrament. Now sacraments differ from legal contracts in that they cannot be broken even by mutual agreement.
This means that the Church is now deeply concerned with the
divorce laws and, believing as it does, that marriage is a sacrament which does not admit of being terminated even by
mutual agreement, it objects to any change in these laws which
would seem to render the marriage contract less binding. It is
the Church which has organized the opposition to all attempts
to bring about changes in the divorce laws.

But it would be unfair to suggest that the Church's control
over marriage and its conversion of what was previously only
a legal contract into a sacrament has been without any benefit
at all to society. A religious sanction is the most powerful of all
sanctions and if, as we believe, marriage is an institution necessary to the welfare of society, then everything which helps to
strengthen it is to be welcomed.

One of the disadvantages of the Church's influence on the
divorce laws is that the Church has always placed great emphasis on the deadly nature of sexual sins and up till 1923 the
only ground which the Anglican Church considered of sufficient importance to warrant the granting of a divorce was that
of adultery. Adultery was sufficient grounds for granting a
divorce to a husband, but not enough for granting a divorce to
a wife. In order that the husband's adultery might be considered
sufficiently deadly to allow of his wife's obtaining a divorce, it
had to be proved that the said husband had committed an in-
cestuous form of adultery, or adultery with bigamy or adultery
with rape, or merely adultery followed by desertion for a
period of two years or more. This difference in the grounds for
divorce was grossly unfair to wives, but fortunately it was rec-
tified by the passing of the Matrimonial Causes Act of 1923,
which made simple adultery sufficient in both sexes. Sir Alan
Herbert's Matrimonial Causes Bill of 1937 extended the grounds

for divorce still further so that they included desertion for three years, cruelty, habitual drunkeness involving also cruelty, incurable insanity and lifelong imprisonment. This Act also added the new provision that no petition could be filed within three years of marriage. The Church of Rome has of course maintained its original attitude to divorce, namely, that as marriage is a holy sacrament it is quite impossible for humanity to tamper with it in any way. Two people have sworn before the altar to accept each other for good and they have no alternative to that of honouring their oath.

If a further rise in the divorce rate is to be avoided it cannot be done by making divorce more difficult to obtain, as some people have advocated, but only by making greater efforts to salvage marriages before they come to divorce. This is so obvious that many people have long been urging that some sort of machinery for settling matrimonial disputes should be set up. In 1935 a Summary Jurisprudence (Domestic Procedure Bill) was actually presented to the House of Lords but unfortunately it had to be withdrawn at the end of the Second Reading. The former London magistrate, Mr. Claude Mullins, has advised that domestic cases which come to the police courts should always be conducted along the lines of conciliation and he has also advised that people should be actively encouraged to bring their private differences for settlement to special domestic courts. If such courts were eventually to be set up, suitable magistrates would have to be appointed to preside over them, aided when this was thought to be necessary, by psychiatrists or by medical men who have had experience in dealing with sexual problems. None of these plans for repairing breaking marriages have as yet been put into practice, but much good work is being done by voluntary and semi-official bodies such as the Marriage Guidance Council.

As has already been said, the Roman Church maintains its

LOVE, MARRIAGE AND THE FAMILY

old uncompromising attitude to divorce and excludes divorcees from the Communion. But the Anglican Church is becoming less implacable to them. A Convocation of Canterbury is shortly to re-examine the Church's position in the light of the fact that many thousands of people are being barred from Church membership by the fact that they have passed through the divorce court. During the last ten years 700,000 people have been divorced and nine out of every fourteen have married again. It has been estimated that rather more than 250,000 of these remarried men and women are ex-members of the Anglican Church.

The position of members of the Anglican Church who have gone through the divorce courts is far from being clear and it differs in different parts of England. Churchgoers who have been divorced, but who have not remarried, can manage to retain their Church membership and can be admitted to Communion if they happen to live in the North of England within the Province of York, but in the South of England and in the Province of Canterbury things are more difficult for them. It has, of course, always been open to divorcees who reside in the South of England to apply for reinstatement but they have been given the impression that they would be regarded with strong disfavour and most are reluctant to make this application. But at the Convocation about to be held a proposal is to be put forward that divorcees can ask for reinstatement even if they have married again, by the very simple method of applying to the parish priest, who will then forward his recommendation to the bishop.

Whatever decisions are eventually reached in the coming Canterbury Convocation there can be no doubt that the leading clergy are becoming thoroughly alarmed at the serious loss the Church is sustaining through its annual "outlawing" of thousands of its former members who have been unfortunate enough to pass through the divorce courts. It is likely that a more tolerant attitude to divorce will in time be adopted and that the parish priest, who is aware of the circumstances which led to the divorce, will be given greater powers of discrimination than he has hitherto possessed. In the opinion of the writer this is all that is at present needed.

I agree with Havelock Ellis that it would be a mistake to be too alarmed about the increase in divorce, for the last thing which will help to preserve the institution of marriage will be to convert it into a prison in which two unhappy and ill-matched people are confined. "It is altogether desirable that marriage unions should be wholesomely honest and real, so that the two partners will not be chained together in a helpless bondage. The dignity of marriage itself demands the freedom of marriage. It should never be possible to believe that two people are living together because they happen to have fallen into a trap together and do not know how to find the way out. Up to the present it still often is possible to believe that. To be an entirely worthy institution, marriage must be a union not only gladly accepted but gladly maintained by each party to it. The more it is dependent on circumstances that are unessential, and even unavowable, the less satisfactory it becomes". (Havelock Ellis, *Sex and Marriage*.)

21

THE TRAGEDY OF INTER-SEX

IN Chapter Six the development of the sex-characteristics was described. It was stated there that the sex of the future individual is determined at the moment of conception by the type of spermatozoon which has brought about the fertilization of the egg-cell or ovum and that at first the embryo is an hermaphrodite, that is to say a creature which possesses the organs of both sexes. The primary glands of sex, that is to say the testicles or ovaries, then begin to take charge of the situation and, by means of their hormones or internal secretions, to push the developing embryo in the direction either of maleness or of femaleness. But sometimes these final stages in the development of the sex characteristics of the child are incomplete either because the hormones of the predominant glands of sex are insufficient for this purpose or else because the body fails to react properly to the hormones. The result of this inadequacy is the birth of an individual of inter-sex, that is to say an individual who possesses some of the characteristics of both sexes.

A true hermaphrodite is an animal which stands midway between the two poles of masculinity and femininity and which possesses a mixture of the primary glands of both sexes, in the way that the early embryo does. True hermaphroditism is an exceedingly rare phenomenon in human life, but unfortunately a mixture of male and female characteristics is not very uncommon. As was pointed out in Chapter Six it is a mistake to look upon the two sexes, masculine and feminine, as two well-defined entities standing widely apart from each other. We should regard them rather as being two conditions which may approach each other so nearly as to cause a great deal of confusion. In other words, no man is one hundred per cent. male, and no woman one hundred per cent. female.

These facts help to explain certain unhappy individuals in whom the confusion of sexual characteristics is sufficiently marked to justify them being placed under the category of "inter-sex". There are several varieties of inter-sexual individuals but only two types need to be considered here, transvestites and certain varieties of homosexuals. Now although for the sake of convenience both of these varieties of "inter-sex" are being considered here together, it must be remembered that the two conditions are quite different; transvestites are not usually homosexuals and homosexuals are not usually transvestites and much harm has been done by failing to distinguish between the two conditions.

Transvestism is a very puzzling state of affairs in which the individual longs to be, and has always longed to be, a member of the opposite sex and who frequently possesses some of the characteristics (physical or psychological or both) of the opposite sex. The word "transvestism" is descriptive only of one of its features, namely, of the urgent desire which many transvestists possess to dress up in the clothes of the opposite sex. Havelock Ellis regarded the term "transvestism" as an unsatisfactory one, because it lays too much emphasis on this intense longing to dress up in the clothes of the opposite sex, which although it is undoubtedly a fact of great importance, is only one of several symptoms of this trouble. He preferred the use of the word "Eonism" which he derived from an historical character, the Chevalier d'Eon de Beaumont, who lived between the years 1728 and 1810 and who acted as Louis XV's accredited agent here in London. It was only after the death of this well-known character in eighteenth-century London society, who had been accepted everywhere as an indubitable woman, that it was discovered that the said Chevalier d'Eon de Beaumont, was actually a man.

True transvestism is comparatively rare but it is a commoner condition than was formerly supposed, and only three things can be said about it with any certainty: first, that little or nothing is known about its causation; second, that it is an exceedingly difficult condition to treat since it very rarely responds to psychotherapy; third, that it causes those who are afflicted by it a great deal of emotional suffering. I am told that a small coterie of these unhappy people sometimes meet in a London restaurant and that if anybody were to look on at this gathering he would be hard put to it to decide the sex of the various members, some of whom are dressed in accordance with their predominant sex and others in harmony with their longings.

Quite distinct from the transvestist is the feminine and effeminate type of homosexual. Whereas medical opinion is now veering in the direction of believing that upbringing is a far more important factor in the causation of homosexuality than is heredity, there is a certain type of homosexual in which heredity is likely to be of considerable importance. I refer to the delicately featured type of homosexual, gentle, immature and diffident, who, if dressed in female clothes, would be readily accepted as a girl. Young men of this type not infrequently remain for good at the homosexual stage of their sexual development and never attain a mature and acceptable pattern of sexual behaviour. Strictly speaking, of course, it is quite impossible to draw a dividing line between the normal and acceptable, and the abnormal and unacceptable pattern of sexual behaviour, because sexuality expresses itself in so many different ways that these words soon lose their meaning. But for present purposes I have accepted the definition of normality given by Dr. Van der

Velde, that is to say, intercourse which takes place between two people of opposite sex which does not entail the infliction of pain or the use of any artificial instrument for the obtaining of sexual gratification.

Man is a gregarious animal and like all animals of this kind he has an intense dislike and even fear of all members of the herd who depart from the standard pattern of appearance and behaviour. Every schoolboy knows how fatal it is to return to school after the holidays wearing some unorthodox article of clothing or behaving in a manner which is not customary in that particular school. But the school is only a miniature of that greater world which the schoolboy will have to enter when he has grown up and in which he will find an equally great, if not an even greater, necessity to conform to the stern rules of the herd. All herds are driven by an overriding instinct to preserve their own integrity, and this means that all members who depart in any way from the accepted standard must be killed or expelled. Human society is equally ruthless and in nothing does it display a greater absence of compassion than in its treatment of those who depart from the approved pattern of sexual appearance and behaviour. It scorns and at the same time is scared by the condition known as "intersex." For the herd a male must be a hundred per cent male and a female a hundred per cent female, whether Nature is prepared to supply this hundred per cent article or not. It demands and it insists on their being no strange mixtures. Yet in Nature herself maleness and femaleness are variables and in between the two extreme types of the intensely masculine male and the intensely feminine female tie various shades of intersex. How the herd regard and treats these in-between variables is illustrated by the two following cases from my own private records.

The first patient is now thirty-eight but I had met him some fifteen years previously. In describing him I shall deliberately

introduce some misleading and non-essentials features in order
to avoid the risk of his being recognized, for he has been per-
secuted enough as it is and now leads a kind of moonlight,
existence, flitting from place to place and seeking to avoid being
seen. Like most eunuchoid individuals he looks very much
younger than he really is and this is a great disadvantage to him
for it allows of his employers retaining his services at a junior
clerk's salary. Recently he attempted to better his position but
it was only necessary for his present employer to murmur the
word "abnormal" into his new employer's ear to bring his
plan of obtaining better pay to nought. Mr. X. was intended
by nature to be a male but at a very early age his male glands
failed and permitted his body to develop some of the characteristics of the female. He does not require to shave and if
dressed in female clothes he would easily pass as a woman.

But what does he himself want to be? He has now given up
trying to decide this question, which formerly was of considerable importance to him. He tells me that at twenty he fell in
love with a girl and wanted to be made into a proper man, but
at twenty-five the pendulum swung in the opposite direction
and feminity became desirable to him. Now it matters very
little to him whether he decides to be a man or a woman for
sexual feeling is on the wane and this is fortunate, for the homosexuals never liked him, nor he them, on the few occasions on
which he met them. Once he tried "petting" a girl, but he
admits that that was a mistake for it aroused desires which he
could never satisfy.

"Tell me", I asked him, "what is the worst thing you have to
bear?"

"It used to be the reactions of other people to me. I was aware
of their shrinking from me as from something unmentionable.
I could never speak to anyone of my guilty secret that in actual
fact was never really a secret. I nearly broke under the strain of

it all once and had to go to a psychologist for a time. But it is not so hard now."

"And what is the greatest difficulty at the present time?"

"It is that I am always a foreigner, but that needs explaining—"

"No it doesn't," I interrupted. "It is only too revealing. What else?"

"Well, you see, I can never have any place in anybody's life and nobody can ever become of real importance to me. I am cut off from all human beings and I can't help feeling a bit lonely at times, can I?"

"You can't," I answered, "and it is more than understandable. But what are your interests apart from your entirely natural interest in your fellow-men?"

"I want to write," he answered, "and the—(here he mentioned a periodical)—is going to give me work that I can do."

There is little that I or anybody else can do for an outcast of this kind beyond encouraging him to face life with all the courage he can summon to his aid, and develop the talents he happens to possess. It is fortunate that he shows some literary ability and is in a position to supplement a junior clerk's poor wages by means of a little occasional journalism. I answered the few remaining questions he wanted to ask of me, the first being as to the rarity or not of his condition. I told him that I had met about twenty men similar to himself but added that there were many others who hid their trouble from their fellow men, and never went near a doctor. We shook hands and he seemed pleased that I looked upon him as a fellow human being—a pathetically small gesture on my part.

Mr. X is only one of many instances of a departure from an acceptable sexual pattern and because he happens to be a comparatively rare type of intersexual he does not constitute a pressing social problem. The problem of the true homosexual is of far greater importance to us, as the following tragic story shows. During the earlier years of the war a youth, then still in his twenties, was brought to see me by his parents in the hope that I would do something to help him. He had been scooped in by one of the Home Office indiscriminate roundups and was about to appear in the dock. Now there are many types of homosexuals, some of whom are curable and others incurable, and in my opinion this boy belonged to the latter class. I therefore wrote the strongest letter possible, stating that with psychological help he could be cured but that if he were sent to prison he would be ruined for life.

Ten years later he came to see me on his own, pleading with me to cure him. He told me that he had been given four years' imprisonment and that during this time such strong pressure had been brought to bear on him that he had yielded himself again to homosexual practices. Nothing was easier than this, sharing a cell, as he did, with three other men and with definite advantages to be gained by consenting.

I no longer see any hope for this man for he is now a neurotic who has lost all respect for himself and is able to face his fellow men only after priming himself with alcohol. He has been given a course of convulsive therapy without any benefit to him and his psychiatrist is now of the opinion that no further treatment is likely to be of any use. Could I suggest any other form of treatment, he asked me. I could suggest nothing. Ten years ago I had written a letter to the effect that a boy could be cured and that he would be ruined if he were sent to prison. In all probability that letter was never read. The law took its course and all hope for that individual went.

Yes, there are few things more brutal than the manner in which the human herd treats departures from a standard sexual pattern which has never existed.

22

APHORISMS ON LOVE AND MARRIAGE

THE poets and great literary artists of the world have crystallized so much uncommon sense and wisdom around the subject of Love and Marriage that a selection of their aphorisms provide an appropriate ending to this book. The following have been selected for this final "curtain."

"Marriage must continually vanquish a monster that devours everything; the monster of habit."—*Balzac*.

"The greater man's soul the deeper is his love."—*Leonardo da Vinci*.

"When two persons love each other, nothing is more imperative and delightful to them than giving: to give always and everything, one's thoughts, one's life, one's body, and all that one has; and to feel the gift and to risk everything in order to be able to give more, still more."—*Guy de Maupassant*.

"Do not begin your marriage with a rape!"—*Balzac*.

"Marriage is joint service; the joint service of husband and wife to one another and the race."—*Rudolph Fischer*.

"Falling in love is the one illogical adventure, the one thing which we are tempted to think as supernatural in our trite and reasonable world."—*R. L. Stevenson*.

"Of all we know in life, only in love in there a taste of the mystical, a taste of ecstasy."—*P. D. Ouspensky*.

"To be a lover is easier than to be a husband, for it is more difficult to show intelligence every day than to make pretty speeches from time to time."—*Balzac*.

"If there are varieties (as of melody) between one erotic occasion and another, a man can always enjoy happiness with one and the same woman."—*Balzac.*

"A cold passionate woman is a woman who has not yet met the man she is bound to love."—*Stendhal.*

"Probably there is no healthy person in whom there does not exist, at some time or other, some kind of supplement to his normal sexual activity, to which we should be justified in giving the name 'perversity'."—*S. Freud.*

"A woman's torment is not man's tyranny—but his indifference."—*Michelet.*

"The husband draws and absorbs his wife's life into his own circle of experience, with irresistible power."—*Goethe.*

"A wife is for her husband that which he has made her."—*Balzac.*

"Let this be your honour! Always to love more than you are loved."—*Nietzsche.*

"A husband's interest and honour alike, enjoins that he should never permit himself a sexual gratification which he has not made his wife desire as well."—*Balzac.*

"The chastest wife can also be the most voluptuous."—*Balzac.*

"To swiftly apprehend the shades and semitones of pleasure in love, to master and develop them, to give them a unique and individual style of expression—therein lies the genius of a husband. Between couples where there is no love this genius is vice. But caresses inspired by love are never unchaste or vicious."—*Anon.*

"All sensible men are of the same opinion about women. And no sensible man ever says what that opinion is."—*Samuel Butler.*

"It is easier to die for a woman one loves than to live with her."—*Byron.*

"If people only made prudent marriages, what a stop to population there would be."—*Thackerary.*

"Keep the eyes open before marriage; and half-shut afterwards."—*D. Fuller.*

"In matters of religion and matrimony I never give any advice; because I will not have anybody's torment in this world or the next laid to my charge."—*Lord Chesterfield.*

"Here is a perfect poem; to awaken a longing, to nourish it, to develop it, to increase it, to stimulate it and to gratify it."—*Balzac.*

"The ignorance of woman's physiology which prevails amongst most men, is boundless and incredible."—*Camille Mariclair.*

"Of all vital questions, none is more important than an understanding of the acts and processes which ensure the perpetuation of life."—*Camille Mariclair.*

"In marriage alone, is a woman completed and fulfilled by the man, and he through her."

"Man and woman compose the fullness of humanity."—*Hippel.*

"If men would give to their married life one-tenth of the trouble and thought they give to their business, the majority of marriages would be happy."—*Robert Haas.*

"All things in woman are a riddle: and all things in woman have one meaning: pregnancy."—*Nietzsche.*

"Sensuousness is no sin, but on the contrary, an adornment to life, a gift of God, like the sweet winds of spring and summer. We should enjoy it, with clear conscience and gladly, and should wish it to all healthy full-grown men and women who want it and need it."—*Gustav Frenssen.*

"What does age matter, if we meet it together?"—*Stendhal.*

"Every natural faculty—and every organic function is such a faculty—by means of exercise, evolution and inheritance can become an Art."—*H. Vaihinger.*

"There is no topic whose interest is at once more humanly

universal and more acutely personal; and at the same time, none on which wise advice is more needed: especially in view of the appalling blindness and follies man has committed in all times and lands, under the pitiless sway of the little blind, wanton god."—*L. de Langle.*

GLOSSARY OF SCIENTIFIC TERMS

AMBI-SEXUAL. Ability to have and enjoy sexual intercourse with either sex.

ANUS. The orifice of the large bowel.

CERVIX. The short passage connecting the vagina and the uterus.

CLITORIS. A small external genital organ, the size of a pea, situated near the entrance to the vagina and corresponding to the penis of the male. Like the latter, it contains erectile tissue and becomes swollen with blood in a state of sexual excitement.

COITUS. The act of sexual congress or intercourse.

COITUS INTERRUPTUS. The withdrawal of the male organ just before ejaculation occurs.

CONCEPTION. The act of fertilization, and production of an embryo, through the union of the male and female germinal cells.

CONTRACEPTIVES. Methods of birth control.

DEVIATIONS OF SEXUALITY. Departure from what is considered to be normal sexual behaviour. The expression of sexual feeling differs in different individuals, but too great a departure from the usual pattern of sexual behaviour is called a deviation.

EJACULATION. The forcible expulsion of semen at the end of the sexual act through the contraction of a number of different muscles. Ejaculation may also occur at the climax of a sexual dream.

EPIDIDYMIS. The coiled tube in which spermatozoa mature after leaving the testis.

EROGENOUS. Literally " Love producing." This refers to certain skin areas the light stimulation of which arouses sexual excitement. The most important of these skin areas are the lips, the breasts and the external genitalia.

FALLOPIAN TUBES. The channel along which the ovum passes on its journey from the ovary to the uterus, or womb. It is lined with cells possessing motile fringes, by the movement of which the ovum is swept onwards.

FETISHISM. The shift of sexual feeling from the totality of the beloved to some small feature or personal belonging.

FOETUS. The developing child before it is viable.

HÆMOPHILIA. A tendency to bleed excessively after some trivial injury.

HETEROSEXUAL. Desire for sexual intercourse with a member of the opposite sex.

HOMOSEXUAL. Desire for sexual intercourse with a member of the same sex.

HYMEN. A variable fold of skin guarding the entrance to the vagina. It is sometimes called "the maidenhead". After it has been ruptured through sexual intercourse a woman is no longer a virgin.

IMPOTENCE. Inability to achieve the sexual act.

319

INSEMINATION, ARTIFICIAL. The placing of a few drops of semen artificially at the entrance to the womb for the purpose of bringing about conception.

MASOCHISM. Sexual satisfaction obtained from submitting to pain or humiliation.

MASTURBATION. The obtaining of sexual gratification by rubbing the genital organ. It is sometimes called self-abuse, a name which implies that it is of an injurious nature. Modern medical opinion is that it is an immature form of sexual expression and only harmful when indulged in to excess.

NIDATION. The process by which the fertilized ovum buries itself in the lining of the uterus.

NEUROSIS. A functional derangement of the central nervous system.

OVARY. The primary sexual gland of the female. In it are stored the ova, or female reproductive cells.

ORGASM. The climax of the sexual act associated with an intensely pleasurable sensation and feeling of satisfaction.

PARTURITION. The process of giving birth.

PENIS. The male external genital organ by means of which the semen is deposited within the female passages.

PERINEUM. The skin and muscle between the anus and the external genital organs.

PLACENTA. The organ by which the foetus is nourished.

PROSTATE. An accessory sexual gland surrounding the male urethra near its junction with the bladder. It is about the size of a chestnut and forms a fluid favourable to the life of the spermatozoa.

SADISM. Sexual satisfaction obtained from the infliction of pain.

SEXUALITY. The possession of sexual desire and capacity.

SPERMATOZOON. The male cell the fusion of which with the ovum gives rise to a new individual. Spermatozoa are formed in the seminiferous tubules of the testes, and millions of them are projected into the female passages at the culmination of the sexual act. They resemble minute tadpoles, and like these animals swim by the movement of their tails.

SPIROCHAETA PALLIDA. The organism responsible for Syphilis.

TESTIS. The primary sexual gland of the male. It has two functions—that of producing spermatozoa and that of forming an internal secretion which is absorbed into the bloodstream.

UTERUS, OR WOMB. A hollow muscular organ within which the embryo develops and from which it is expelled at labour.

VAGINA. The female genital passage leading to the womb.

VAS DEFERENS. The duct along which the spermatozoa pass on their journey from the testicle to the urethra. The walls of the vas deferens are muscular, and waves of contraction pass along them during the later stages of intercourse. These contractions propel the testicular secretion towards the urethra.

WASSERMAN REACTION. The blood-test for active syphilis.